551.4   Silverberg
Si   The World of Coral

DATE DUE			

GAYLORD M-2   PRINTED IN U.S.A.

551.4   Silverberg   80
Si   The World of Coral

Date Due

MAR 19			

Demco 38-297

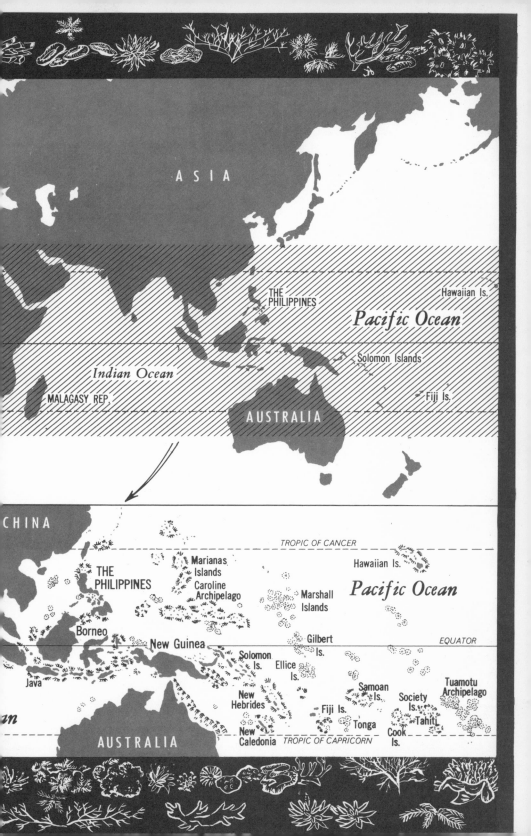

The World
of Coral

Books by Robert Silverberg

Robert Silverberg

The World of Coral

Photographs by
Barbara Silverberg

Duell, Sloan and Pearce
New York

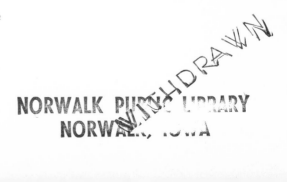

First edition

DUELL, SLOAN & PEARCE
AFFILIATE OF
MEREDITH PRESS

Library of Congress Catalog Card Number: 65-24858

MANUFACTURED IN THE UNITED STATES
OF AMERICA FOR MEREDITH PRESS

VAN REES PRESS   •   NEW YORK

For Boyd—who prefers the sun and the shore

Contents

The World
of Coral

1.

The Garden in the Sea

The sea is calm today. We stand on a crescent beach of pink-white sand, watching the water lap against the shore. Behind us are the sea-grape trees, with their big round leaves, and the poisonous manchineel trees, whose sap burns the skin. Before us is the sea.

The water, sparkling brilliantly in the hot sunlight, is crystal-clear at our feet. Offshore, its hue is green. Looking out to the distance, we see the deeper water, which is blue. A white line of foam marks the boundary where green water gives way to blue. Out there, at the edge of the deeps, a coral reef rises almost to the surface, and the foam we see is the breaking surf sweeping over the reef. On the shoreward side of the reef, the water is shallow; sunlight bouncing through it gives it its emerald color. We are about to swim to the reef, to enter the strange and beautiful world of coral.

Although it is winter now in the northern part of the world, the air here is warm, and we have no fears of taking a swim in February. We are in the West Indies—on Jamaica, perhaps, or Antigua, or St. John. This is a place where winter never comes.

Beach scene, West Indies

The tropical sun glows all the year round, and the land and water remain warm. The water must be warm, for the tiny animals that have built the mighty coral reef can flourish only in a kind climate.

We walk toward the water, now.

We walk clumsily, for our feet are encased in bulky rubber flippers. On land, they get in our way; but once we are in the water, the flippers will help us glide easily over the coral formations, and they will protect our feet against the creatures that are armed with stings or sharp spines. Breathing-masks cover our faces. Plastic tubes jut up over our heads. They are our snorkels. As we swim, the tops of the snorkel tubes will remain above the water, feeding a steady supply of air to us. Before snorkels became popular, most people could see coral reefs only by looking down through glass-bottomed boats. Now it is easy to get close to the world of coral. Anyone who can swim can use a snorkel; ten minutes of practice is all that is needed.

We make sure that our masks fit snugly. We grin at one another as our adventure begins. Then we step into the water, and start to swim out to the reef.

Faces down, peering through our masks, we see the sandy bottom three or four feet below us. The clear water magnifies everything, bringing it much closer than it really is, and for a moment we think we are going to scrape the bottom with our bellies as we swim. Then we glance at our hands in the water, and see that they are a third larger than we know them to be, and we stop worrying about hitting bottom.

Tiny minnows swim in clouds through the water, thousands of them. We see little turrets in the sand, perhaps made by worms, perhaps by crabs, for the lifeless-looking zone just offshore is actually well populated under the sand. We keep swimming, and soon the water is a little deeper, though it is just as clear as before, and we can see easily to the bottom. The sunlight makes glittering patterns on the sandy floor.

That floor is changing, now. Thick tufts of grass carpet it. Here and there in the grass are round sea urchins, covered with short white spines and looking very much like pincushions. We see a few fish grazing in the grass; they pay no attention to us. A starfish lies sprawled out on a sandy patch, its five thick arms moving slowly, exploring the bottom. Not far away we see a gray-white shell, big and elaborate, with a number of knobs and bumps on the upward-pointing spire. We recognize it as a conch, a huge water-dwelling snail. We have seen the polished shells of conchs decorating the gardens of many homes on our island.

We continue into ever deeper water. Swimming is effortless; the Caribbean's waters keep us buoyant, and the air in our masks helps, too. The flippers push us swiftly through the water. There are no waves. It becomes easy to forget that we are swimming at all, and it seems as though we are flying through the air, looking down at a fascinating world below us.

That world grows different again. We are past the grassy zone and are beginning to sight some coral. On a boulder to our left we see a mustard-colored crust of "stone," curving and recurving so that it looks like the battlement of some miniature fortress. We eye it with respect, for it is a stinging coral known as *fire coral*, well equipped to defend itself against sightseers such as ourselves. On the sea floor below the boulder we spy another troublemaker of the reef: a big black sea urchin, whose spines are evil-looking needles more than six inches long. The white-spined sea urchin we met in the grass could have done us no harm, but this black-spined one is a menace. The sharp spines break at the slightest touch and pierce the skin, causing painful infections. Glancing around, we see that the long-spined urchins are everywhere, and now we realize why it is wise to wear rubber flippers in these waters.

A few yards away is more coral, a green dome about two feet across, whose surface is covered with meandering grooves. It looks like a human brain, with all its wrinkles and folds, and so we know we are meeting *brain coral*. As we hover over it, we notice that it seems to be covered with flowers. Gay petals of red and yellow flutter from crannies on the coral dome. But as we wave a flipper at the "flowers," they disappear, whisking into tiny caves on the coral's surface! They are not plants at all. What we have seen are the gills of tubeworms, who have made their homes on the brain coral. When danger appears, they quickly vanish. We wait, and soon the colorful tubeworm gills poke cautiously into view once more.

The bottom is still sandy. Coral clumps are scattered here and there, but they are not close together. The fish are becoming

more numerous, though. They pay little heed to the bulky intruders who drift along the roof of their world. We see a slender,
silvery fish just below the surface ahead of us—a needlefish,
whose long beak seems to cut a path for it through the water.
Below, on the sand, a sting ray takes alarm and goes flapping
away, its dangerous tail-spine clearly visible as it retreats. Another fish of the sand is there, but it does not retreat at all; it
is the lizardfish, whose mottled gray skin makes it almost invisible as it rests motionless on the bottom. Near it is another
camouflaged fish that we nearly overlook, a sand flounder, flat
against the sandy floor.

The water is deeper here. We look up and back at the shore,
and see that we are several hundred feet from land. But the
white line of surf marking the crest of the coral reef is still well
ahead of us.

As we swim, we discover that we are entering the true domain
of coral at last. Closer to shore, we saw only scattered outcroppings. Here, the coral grows thickly and closely, forming a maze
that in places reaches almost to the surface.

We are entering the reef.

It is a startling sight. Ahead of us in every direction stretches
an eerie garden in the sea, with "trees," "shrubs," "plants," and
"flowers." But the trees are of stone, while the shrubs and plants
and flowers are all animals. We see a riot of colors: greens and
oranges, lilacs and reds, purples, turquoises, yellows. There is
such an abundance of life here that we are dazzled by it.

We recognize brain coral here, but the green domes are seven
and eight feet across, now, and must weigh thousands of pounds.
Here is fire coral, forming a fantasylike crust over the giant
boulders. The water is a little rougher here; we sway with the
currents, and the fish sway too, fish of every color, every shape,
moving in the water like autumn leaves swept by the breeze.
A delicate, lacy *sea fan*, four feet high, sprouts from the bottom

Staghorn coral

and flutters from side to side as the currents strike it. Orange-toned *staghorn coral*, looking fragile and unreal, rises in criss-cross patterns everywhere. Not at all fragile-looking is the massive *elkhorn coral*, also orange, whose bulky branches are thick and heavy, forming great shelflike layers as they reach toward the surface. Just ahead of us is a whole forest of elkhorn coral, its branches interlocking so that our path is blocked. We have to turn and find a different passageway through the coral maze.

Here are big boulders of green *star coral*, and mounds of white rock that must have been living coral once, and grottoes and caverns of stone that was formed by soft creatures the size of a pinhead. We hover over everything, and the sensation that we are flying becomes more intense. We seem to be staring down on a hillside thick with bushes. Those wavy, fernlike "bushes" are corals, though, colonies of tiny animals; we call them *gorgonians*. There are many kinds of gorgonians, some thin and feathery, others thick and sturdy. Rainbow-hued fish chase through the soft branches. Two long feelers jut from a coral cavern on the reef floor, and we know that a big lobster lies resting there. In another opening in the coral we spy the toothy head of a moray eel. He looks dangerous and unfriendly, and he is; but like nearly all the creatures of the reef, the moray eel will not bother us if we do not bother him. So we skirt his cave and swim onward through the amazing garden in the sea.

The water is more than thirty feet deep out here, but it is nearly as clear as it was just offshore. We can see down to the

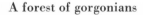

A forest of gorgonians

bottom without difficulty. And the coral is gigantic. A vast tree of elkhorn coral rises from the bottom and reaches almost to the surface. Its immense trunk must be twenty feet high, and its branches spread out in all directions. Big brain corals and star corals are everywhere. We swim through channels bordered by coral walls covered over with many kinds of life-forms—sponges, algae, gorgonians, all hiding the coral rock beneath. A close look tells us that every part of the reef has its inhabitants; we spy tiny green crabs, a wonderful array of gaudy tube-worms, and the small brown form of an octopus on the rocks.

We are near the boundary of the deeps, now. Peering through the intricate and interlocking coral growths, we see blue water ahead where the reef ends. We can see the flattened tops of the elkhorn corals right at the surface, and when we rise, we are able to see the white foam boiling over the reef as the outer sea lashes against it. Beyond is the blue water. The big fish live out there, the game fish, shark and barracuda and marlin. They are too bulky to venture into the complicated tangle that is the reef, and so generally they remain outside it, entering only at the widest channels to find a meal of fish.

We do not trespass on their dominion. Instead, we turn and swim slowly toward shore, retracing our path through the garden of coral, now and then finding ourselves in a dead end where the reef comes so near the surface that we cannot swim over it without the risk of getting scratched by the sharp rocks. When we find ourselves penned in that way, we simply back up and take a different channel; there are many of them. A boat could not easily get through this reef, but we swimmers can.

And so back we go, from the zone of big coral to the zone of small coral, and then into the grassy kingdom of the conch and starfish, and on to the bright, sun-dappled, sandy-bottomed zone near shore. Finally we stand and wade ashore, clumsy in our flippers.

We shed them, and our masks and snorkels too, and stand a little dazed in the sunlight, feeling the sand of the beach under our feet. Our swim has lasted less than an hour. Already, it seems almost like a dream. Did we really soar effortlessly over that garden in the sea? Those dazzling colors, that dizzying complexity of life—did we actually see them, or was it all a prank of the imagination?

We look seaward. Once more we see the green water of the shallows, the dark shadows of coral, the white line of distant foam, and the blueness of the deep sea stretching to the horizon. It was all real. For a brief while we were guests of the coral world. We have truly seen those caverns and grottoes, those stunning hues, those magical shapes.

We are willing to believe it all. But how did that garden get there? Who built the coral caverns? Creatures the size of a pinhead, we are told. Is it possible? We want to know the story. We have come into the coral world as strangers, as intruders. Now, once again on land, curiosity takes command of us, and a hundred questions bubble up at once. There are many things to know. But the most basic, the most important of the questions are the ones that deal with the coral creatures themselves, the architects of that wonderland in the sea.

2.

Builders of the Reef

A coral reef is a community. It harbors a population of many
hundreds of different forms of life, some so small they cannot
be seen with the unaided eye, others as big as the fearsome
twelve-foot sharks that patrol the outer rim of the reef. Clams,
shrimps, scallops, squids, octopuses, many kinds of worms,
fish of a hundred sorts, sea urchins, starfish, snails, lobsters,
sponges, crabs—all these dwell on the reef, and many more
besides. Though a coral reef may look confusing at first glance,
it is actually tightly organized. Each creature has its place in
the scheme. Each has its own home, its own hunting ground.

Without the coral, though, there would be no community.
The solid stone of the coral provides the foundation for the life
of the reef. The tiny coral-building creatures, in building homes
for themselves, also create shelter for all the dwellers on the
reef. More than that: as we will see, the coral-building creatures
produce whole islands, in time, that serve as homes for human
beings.

If we were looking at a single coral creature, we would find
it hard to understand how reefs and coral islands could ever be

built. We would see a soft, almost transparent little blob of jelly, a fraction of an inch long. Simple, tiny animals such as these are responsible for the stony monuments of the coral seas.

An individual coral animal is called a *polyp*. The word is derived from a Greek term meaning "many-footed." Originally it was applied to the octopus, which does indeed have many feet; the French word for octopus, taken from Greek, is *poulpe*. In the eighteenth century, French naturalists studying coral thought that the coral creatures, which have a crown of waving tentacles, looked like little octopuses. So they called them *poulpes*, or polyps, also.

Coral polyps belong to the group of animals known as the *coelenterates*, which also includes such forms as jellyfish and sea anemones. That word also comes from the Greek, and means "hollow-gutted." Coelenterates are extremely simple animals that consist, basically, of a hollow tube closed at one end. The open end of a polyp is its mouth, fringed with tentacles that help to capture food. The entire hollow center of the polyp is its digestive cavity. Food enters through the mouth, is digested inside, and the waste products are spurted out the same opening through which the food entered. The polyp is made up of just two layers of cells, one layer forming the inside and one the outside of the tube.

Some coelenterates, like the jellyfish and the small fresh-water animal called the *hydra*, live a free, roving existence. So do coral polyps, when they are young. But the corals quickly settle down and build a permanent house for themselves. They draw calcium carbonate from the water they live in and shape it to form a solid structure around them. Calcium carbonate is a white, stony substance that takes many forms on land. Chalk is one form. Marble, from which great buildings and statues are made, is calcium carbonate. So is limestone, the rock that makes up many of the mountains of the American West.

A sketch of fire coral from Dana's *Corals and
Coral Islands* (1872)

Limestone and other mineral forms of calcium carbonate tend
to dissolve under chemical action. Over a great period of time,
much limestone has broken down into lime (calcium oxide),
which enters the sea. The coral polyps, like all living animals,
give off carbon dioxide. This combines with the dissolved lime
in the water to produce calcium carbonate once more, and the
polyps are able to extract this substance and create limy skeletons for themselves. Sea water does not readily dissolve calcium
carbonate.

If we pick up a piece of dead coral cast up on a seashore, we
get a good idea of the polyp's house. We see a number of cup-

shaped depressions, usually, and a close look shows that each is divided into small partitions that seem to be the spokes of a wheel. When the coral was alive, each of these cups was the home of a single polyp. The outer side of the polyp's body is marked with ridges called *mesenteries,* and the shape of the limy cup follows the pattern of the mesenteries. Vertical plates are formed in these ridges, and are known as *septa.* They remain after the polyp dies and decays.

New polyps are spawned by the thousands, through sexual reproduction. There are no "male" or "female" polyps; a single polyp produces both sperm cells and egg cells, though not at the same time. When they are fully developed, the sperm cells are cast into the water. Other polyps, constantly pumping food-laden water through their bodies, take them in. When a sperm cell encounters a fully-developed egg cell within a polyp, fertilization takes place.

The fertilized eggs remain inside the parent polyp for a while. When it is time for them to hatch, the polyp contracts its walls and the young polyps spurt out into the water. Great numbers are born at once, but few of them survive. Many creatures find the newborn polyps a tasty meal.

The young polyps, which are called *planulae,* are equipped with tiny, whiplike hairs that allow them to swim. The pear-shaped planulae swim until they come to a place that is suited for a permanent dwelling. Some of the planulae find their homes in a few hours. Others drift for days before settling down. Most are eaten or are simply swept into the open sea.

When a planula finds a suitable place, such as a rock, it cements itself down by giving off a sticky liquid at its narrow end. Now it has the form of a hollow vase standing upright. Six knobs appear at the rim of the mouth, and these become tentacles. Soon, six more appear, and more after that. The mesenteries also begin to take shape.

As soon as it is safely attached, the polyp begins to grow its skeleton. Drawing calcium carbonate from the water, it manufactures limestone in the form of six radiating bars below and outside its body. These bars grow upward, fitting into the folds of the mesenteries, until the polyp is living in a stony cup with six spokelike partitions, the septa. The upper part of the polyp projects from the cup. Its tentacles lash the water, capturing even smaller swimming animals and dragging them in to be digested. To stun their prey, the polyps have stinging cells between their tentacles.

As the coral polyp flourishes and grows larger, it brings new polyps into life. This is usually done sexually by developing sperm and egg cells. However, a polyp can reproduce in another way—a way that produces the vast coral reefs.

This is by budding. New polyps, exactly like the parent, sprout from the sides of the old ones. They do not break loose and take up independent existences, as is true in the budding of free-swimming polyps such as the hydra. Rather, they remain at the parent's side, building limy skeletons of their own.

The form that the skeleton takes depends on the type of coral polyp. There are about 2,500 different species of corals, and each builds a skeleton of a distinct type. If the coral is a branching form, such as staghorn or elkhorn coral, the new polyps will grow out at an angle on each side of the parent. These new polyps will bud in turn, producing ever wider branches. In the coral types that form round boulders, such as brain and star coral, the new polyps grow upward alongside the old ones instead of branching away from them.

All the polyps continue to bud and to grow. What began with a single, microscopic, pear-shaped planula rapidly comes to be a colony of thousands of polyps, all clustered around the same base. Growing upward and outward, the polyps extend their limy skeletons all the time, so that they come to live on the outer edge of a bulky mass of stone. They form new floors of stone beneath themselves as they grow. If we cut a clump of coral down the middle we would find it to be composed of a great many stone tubes divided into chambers, with the living polyps in the outermost chamber.

In this way, huge structures of stone are constructed by animals no bigger than pinheads. The reefs grow slowly but steadily. Scientists have studied the rate of coral growth in great detail. One report showed that a shallow-water reef might grow upward at a rate of about a foot every $11\frac{1}{2}$ years, so that in a thousand years the reef would be almost a hundred feet thick. Each kind of coral grows at its own speed. Some of the branching corals add an inch or two a year; others grow nearly twice as fast. A big coral boulder on a Pacific reef was found to increase in diameter by thirty inches over twenty-three years.

Other forms of life aid in creating the reefs. Shells of clams and oysters are cemented to the coral boulders. Tubeworms and their relatives build limy homes that add to the bulk of the reefs. The bodies of starfish and sea urchins and sponges contain lime too, and when these animals die they contribute to the rising structure. Even plants play important roles: certain algae, related to the seaweeds, have the ability to draw calcium carbonate from the water as coral polyps do. They encrust the reefs, forming a horny coating that serves to cement the shells and sand and coral fragments together into a tight, solid structure.

At the same time, enemies of the reef are busy breaking it down again. There is a kind of sponge that is able to dissolve the rock of the reef. Snails and worms bore into the coral, killing the polyps as they drill their tunnels. Many fish munch on the reef, crushing the limestone to get at the polyps within. The sea itself attacks the reef; in stormy weather, waves batter at the coral, breaking huge pieces loose.

So the reef does not always increase; if it did, every island

Skeleton of a sea fan

where coral can grow at all would be surrounded by an impassable belt of stone. The reef is in a state of constant change. On the Pacific island of Samoa, for example, a scientist found that the polyps were adding about 840,000 pounds of limestone to the reef each year, but that four times as much stone was being removed every year by the action of boring animals and water currents. That reef, then, has been shrinking for some time. Others, in more favorable conditions, are in a cycle of growth.

As S. J. Hickson, an English scientist who devoted more than fifty years to the study of coral, wrote: "It seems probable that a reef never remains perfectly stationary. It is always slowly advancing or retreating. . . . It is like a huge living pulsating organism slowly stretching out an arm here and withdrawing one there, in some places showing youth and vigor, in others disease and death, capable of withstanding the rough buffetings of storms and surf and yet extremely sensitive to some of the slighter changes of environmental conditions."

The reef-builders need very special conditions in order to do their work. Coral itself is found all over the world; there are corals off the New England coast, corals in the chilly waters off Scandinavia and Great Britain, corals that live at depths of many hundreds of feet in the sea. But these are not the reef-building kinds. They build colonies that remain isolated and small. The true stony corals that construct the great reefs are found only in the tropics. They must have ocean water with a temperature above 70° F. at all times. It must be clear water, for they are killed by mud or sand, and it must be water in constant motion, to bring a steady food supply and to carry away the silt that might otherwise be deposited on the polyps. It must be shallow water; reefs do not form below depths of 150 feet, and growth is best in water fifteen to thirty feet deep.

So we would not expect to find living coral reefs at the bottom of a deep sea, nor at the borders of Antarctica, nor in stagnant bays. Reefs do not grow where rivers reach the sea, either, for the river carries with it a load of silt and mud, as well as a stream of cold, fresh, polyp-killing water. Only where conditions of light, temperature, and water are ideal do reefs develop—in the West Indies, in the Pacific and Indian Oceans, and along the shores of the Red Sea.

The reefs are built from limestone, which is a white mineral. Dead coral is almost always a chalky white. Yet our snorkel tour of the reef showed us that the living coral was brightly colored. The reefs of the West Indies are chiefly green or dull orange, but on the much larger reefs of the Pacific the palette is more varied, and we find blue corals, pink corals, yellow, lavender, auburn, and red. If limestone is white, what gives the reefs their gaiety of color?

The polyps do, to some degree. Some are colorless, but others are brown, yellow, green, or pink. An important factor in the color of living coral, however, is the presence of microscopic algae that live within the polyps. These plants tint the corals with their own hues. They also provide a major scientific puzzle.

There are many examples in nature of two or more forms of life coming together for mutual benefit. This is called *symbiosis,* from the Greek words meaning "living together." An interesting kind of symbiosis involves a small coral of the Indian Ocean, *Heterocyathus,* and a worm with the scientific name of *Aspidosiphon. Heterocyathus* is not a reef coral; it forms miniature colonies about a third of an inch high on the sandy ocean bottom. Since it has no way of attaching itself to the floor, the coral could be overturned by currents and smothered in the sand. But the worm serves as an anchor! *Aspidosiphon* makes its home in the discarded shell of a snail. The coral polyp settles on the outside of the shell and grows until it completely encases it, leaving only a small hole through which the worm's head can reach. The worm feeds in the sand, thus rooting the coral and protecting it from being overturned, while the coral provides a snug housing for the worm. So both creatures benefit from this highly unusual arrangement.

The symbiosis of algae and coral polyps is more complicated and harder to understand. The algae dwell in great numbers in the tissues of the polyps. The polyps, being animals, take in oxygen from the water around them and give off carbon dioxide as a waste product. Algae, like other plants, make use of carbon dioxide in the process known as *photosynthesis*, from which they draw the energy to live. They convert the carbon dioxide to starch, giving off oxygen in the process.

The arrangement is useful for the algae, who get shelter from it and a constant source of the carbon dioxide that they need in photosynthesis. But it is not so easy to see what benefit the polyps get. They seem to get enough oxygen without using the oxygen the algae produce; nor do they seem to depend on the algae for food, since they eat only animal life. Experiments show that the polyps can grow quite well without their algae companions, at least under laboratory conditions. Possibly in the crowded reef the polyps *do* need the extra oxygen provided by the algae. Whatever the reason, reef corals and algae are always found together. The whole polyp–algae relationship is still being studied by biologists.

Photosynthesis can take place only in light. That is one reason why the reef-building corals must grow in shallow water—for the sake of their algae. Sunlight does not penetrate much below 150 feet, even in the extremely clear water where coral grows, and the algae "tenants" of the polyps would not be able to function. For the same reason, most polyps grow with their mouths toward the surface, so that their algae can receive the sunlight. A few reef corals grow on the underside of boulders, with the polyps facing downward, and these do not have any algae in them at all.

The algae and the polyps keep a convenient feeding schedule. During the day, when the sun is shining, the polyps pull their tentacles in and huddle down in their stony cups. This exposes the tissues containing the algae to the sunlight. They drink in the

light, using it to manufacture food from the carbon dioxide
produced by the polyps, and giving off oxygen. When we go
snorkeling in daylight, we are therefore unable to see the polyps.
If we touch the outer surface of a piece of coral, it will feel
hard and dead; the polyps are hidden.

At night the polyps awaken. Their tentacles expand and
grope through the water for the minute animals that serve as
polyp food. Their mouths gape open. The color of the coral
changes now that the polyps are unfolded. Instead of the stony
ridges and pits and folds of the coral surface, a nighttime
swimmer sees the tiny star-shaped "flowers" that are the polyps,
gaily colored, busy hunting for dinner. Since the polyps are sensitive to touch, they pull their tentacles into the stone cups if a

Finger coral

Finger coral (left) ; gorgonian (right)

hand comes in contact with them. When morning comes, the polyps retreat, and it is the turn of the algae to feed again.

Snorkeling at night is a difficult and dangerous activity. The swimmer must carry his own light, and he must make his way over shadowy reefs that could slash him badly if he blundered into them. Except for scientists, then, few visitors to the coral waters see the polyps in action. The lifeless-seeming stone formations of daytime look quite different when the thousands of soft polyps have emerged after dark. A few types of coral polyp do remain open during the day, though. *Finger coral*, a small form usually found close to shore, is one that does. The polyps are small, rubbery projections, a fraction of an inch long, that pull out of sight when touched.

Elkhorn coral

The food of the polyps is known as *plankton*. Plankton is a kind of soup made up of millions upon millions of almost invisible organisms drifting through the water. Much of the plankton is plant life, but the carnivorous polyps ignore that. Their busy tentacles and stinging cells lie in wait for the delicate, transparent plankton animals. Included are the young of many of the reef creatures—baby shrimp, starfish, sea urchins, crabs, even the planulae of corals. All night long the polyps prey on this rich feast, until the first rays of the morning sun slice through the clear water and signal the beginning of the day.

Of the many kinds of coral found throughout the world, from the Arctic to the Antarctic, several hundred exist on coral reefs. The casual snorkeler, though, is likely to notice only a few types.

Skeleton of elkhorn coral

Probably the most dramatic are the huge elkhorn corals. These are found on reefs throughout the world. They get their name from their resemblance to the flattened antlers of the elk, but, because of their branching shape, elkhorn corals are often compared to trees. When found in twenty feet or more of water, they may have main stems nearly a foot thick, and branches that reach out across many yards. The branches sometimes take the form of big, flat, shelflike fronds; a swimmer can stand on one to rest. Elkhorn corals tend to grow in great abundance, forming whole "forests" whose interwoven boughs create an impassable barrier that may stretch for hundreds of feet in the West Indies, or for many miles on the reefs of the Pacific. Frequently, elkhorns grow upward to within a few inches of the surface, and at low tides their flat limbs can be seen jutting above the water. Enough water washes over the exposed coral to keep the polyps alive until the tide rises again.

Though elkhorn coral formations are often enormous and almost overpowering in their bulk, the polyps that build them are extremely small. A snorkeler who pauses to examine the surface of an elkhorn branch will see that it is covered with hundreds of minute puckered openings. Each of these is the home of a polyp. After dark, tentacles will appear, but the entire visible part of the polyp is only a tenth of an inch long.

Elkhorn coral is thick and strong, and is found in many parts of the reef, even on the outer edge where the full strength of the deep sea can batter against it. Much more delicate is a related antlerlike form, staghorn coral, whose slender branches break easily. Staghorn corals grow best in sheltered situations. Too close to shore, they would be smashed by the surf; too far out, they could not withstand the surge of the sea. If they grew too close to the surface, they would be broken by the ebb and flow of the tide. So we usually find staghorn corals in fairly deep and quiet water.

The polyps of staghorn and elkhorn corals are very similar, though the skeletons they build take different shapes. What governs the form of the coral colony, above all else, is the degree of roughness of the water it grows in. Rough-water corals are dense and compact. In deep, quiet water, where the corals can grow undisturbed by the tides and waves of the surface, the shapes become more fanciful and elegant. The cups holding the polyps are more conspicuous in calm-water corals, too; in the rough-water forms, they are nearly flush with the surface of the stone, to give greater protection to the polyps.

Staghorn and elkhorn corals found on the reefs of the West Indies are always a rusty orange color, because of the staining of the limestone by the algae present in the polyps. The orange stain is found only on the surface, as we discover if we look at a coral branch that has been broken off; the inner stone is white. Coral brought to shore bleaches to the white color of the limestone after the polyps and algae die.

In the Pacific, the various antler corals are much more colorful. The Australian zoologist, T. C. Roughley, gives us this description of the staghorns of the Great Barrier Reef that runs along the eastern coast of Australia for more than a thousand miles:

"The colors of the staghorns are among the most beautiful of all corals. A whole colony may be a uniform hue, perhaps blue, heliotrope, lavender, purple, red, pink, green, brown, yellow, and an infinite variety of intermediate shades, or the tips of the branches may assume an entirely different color to form a pleasing and beautiful contrast. The branches may be a bright green with lilac tips; pale yellow with rose pink tips; light buff with pale blue tips; straw-colored with heliotrope tips; bright pink with lemon yellow tips; and a wide range of similar combinations." Roughley also tells how during strong gales staghorn corals are broken and swept ashore: "Their dead and decaying branches may be seen piled up on the weather side of many islands to a depth of several feet and a width of several yards, forming a rampart hundreds of yards long."

Quite different from the branching corals are the solid,

Brain coral skeleton

boulder-forming kinds. Brain coral is an impressive member of this group.

It gets its name from its resemblance to the human brain, which is covered with a maze of valleys and ridges that wander in all directions. In the growth of brain corals, the polyps do not bud; they simply divided in half. They separate from the mouth downward, and almost as soon as one polyp has split at the mouth, each of the two new ones begins to divide also. Thus the separation of the polyps is never really complete; they remain joined at the stomachs. What develops is a long ribbonlike colony of polyps with many mouths and tentacles that form parallel lines several inches long. One colony of these joined polyps,

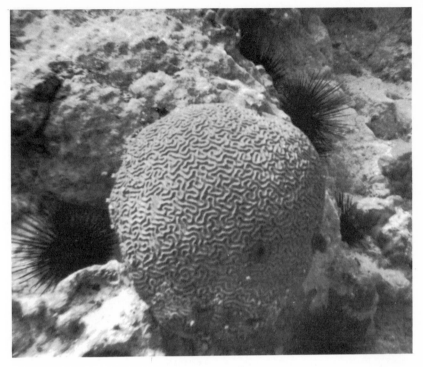

Brain coral

twisting and winding as it grows, meets other colonies, and in time a boulder of brain coral emerges.

These boulders are huge. Some of them are twelve to fifteen feet in diameter, and weigh several tons. The heart of each boulder is dead white limestone rock; since polyps must be able to reach water, only the outside layer of any coral formation is alive. The polyps are green with brown tentacles, but they remain out of sight during the day, and the brain coral has a dark green color then. When the polyps are unfolded, the boulder seems to be covered with a dark brown slime.

Another boulder-forming family is the group of star corals. There are many kinds of star corals, and most of them build

Star coral skeleton

rounded dome-shaped colonies that can reach great size. The polyps are separate. Their cups often stand out a fraction of an inch from the coral structure, giving the boulders a roughened feel. The small stony partitions known as septa can be clearly seen, and their star-shaped patterns give these corals their family name. In some star corals the polyps are crowded together and take on sharp-cornered shapes; some are four-sided, some five-sided, as can be observed in dead skeletons of star coral that wash ashore.

These massive stony corals—elkhorn, brain, star, and several others—are the chief building blocks of the coral reef. Scientists class them as *madrepore* corals, a name that means "mother of stone." The big madrepores provide the basic strength of the reef. Growing for century after century, they are seemingly immortal. So long as their surroundings remain favorable, the polyps continue to divide and increase. A change in growing conditions can kill a coral colony or even an entire reef. But when favorable conditions return, free-swimming young polyps appear, attach themselves to the dead skeletons of the old corals, and begin building new structures on top of them.

Though the strength of the reef comes from these stony corals, the life and beauty and complexity of the world of coral comes from other growths that are not nearly so huge nor so permanent. Some of these are small madrepore corals, but most belong in different classes.

One unusual stony coral, found in the Pacific and Indian Ocean reefs but not in the West Indies, is *mushroom coral*. This madrepore does not form colonies at all, nor does it attach itself to the bottom. A single polyp of mushroom coral grows until it has the general size and shape of a dinner plate. Some mushroom corals are a foot in diameter, and the thick tentacles, when fully outstretched, are as long as three inches. The radiating plates or septa, which are also unusually large, give the coral the look of the many-gilled underside of a mushroom. When it is young, a mushroom coral grows upward on a small stalk rooted to the bottom, increasing the resemblance to a toadstool. After reaching a diameter of an inch or so, it breaks from its stalk and thereafter lies free on the sand of the bottom.

It might seem that the mushroom coral would be in great danger of smothering as shifting currents move the sand about. However, this big polyp has whiplike hairs called *cilia*, which it uses to brush away any sand that might land on it. Even if the mushroom coral is completely buried by sand, it can push its way upward into the open by flailing at the sand with its cilia. It is so very different from the other stony corals that early naturalists believed it was a real mushroom that had fallen into the sea and somehow turned to stone. In the seventeenth century, a Dutch-born naturalist living in the East Indies was able to prove that this coral was not related at all to mushrooms, and was more like a jellyfish housed in stone—but even he did not recognize it as a coral, and its real nature was not understood until 1830.

Some of the most attractive members of the reef community belong to the group of "soft" corals, or *alcyonarians*. These take their name from *Alcyonium,* a spongy, flexible coral found in cool waters and known commonly as dead-man's-fingers. This coral does not grow on reefs itself, but other alcyonarians do, and are important features of the reef world.

Alcyonarian polyps have eight tentacles apiece, and eight mesenteries. This sets them apart from the madrepores, or stony corals, whose tentacles and mesenteries grow in groups of six. More notably, most alcyonarians are unable to build thick limestone skeletons. Some of them can form small slivers of limestone, which are scattered through their tissues, giving them a tough but flexible skeleton. In a few forms, these slivers are packed so closely that the corals seem at first glance to be of the

Gorgonians (foreground)

madrepore kind. A good many alcyonarians make their skeletons from a substance called *keratin,* which is similar to horn.

Soft corals are everywhere on the reef. Sometimes they grow so thickly that they smother the hard coral to which they attach themselves. They often have wavy, fluttering branches that ripple and sway in the currents, and it is hard to realize that these are colonies of thousands of small polyps rather than shrubs and bushes.

The horny, shrublike kinds of alcyonarians form a special group of their own. They are the *gorgonians,* a name that comes from Greek mythology. It refers to the Gorgons, those sinister ladies who had writhing snakes for hair. The gorgonians frequently outnumber the true corals on the reef. One common kind

is the sea fan, which forms flattened, upright colonies several
feet tall. The lovely sea fans, green or violet in color, are firmly
anchored to the reef floor, and bend gracefully with each movement of the water. A sea fan has long ribs that are cross-ribbed
by smaller ones, giving it a lacy look, and from every rib of the
fan hungry polyp-mouths extend to capture the plankton animals
that drift through the water.

Other gorgonians form big, shrublike tufts whose feathery
branches spread in all directions, whirling and bending as the
currents surge. These are the *sea whips*, which have many varieties. Some are as tall as a man, and have branches an inch or
more in thickness; others are much smaller, with tiny "twigs."
Their flexible but strong skeletons house throngs of polyps,
which remain open in daytime, popping out of sight only when
some passing swimmer touches and disturbs them. Orange, lilac,
purple, yellow, brown, and buff are the most common colors
of these bushy, many-branched animal colonies.

The gorgonians provide homes for many of the small creatures
of the reef. A little snail called the flamingo tongue often lives
on sea fans, crawling slowly from branch to branch without
harming the polyps. Other animals live in crannies and crevices
at the base of a gorgonian. Once, in the Virgin Islands, I found
a gorgonian that had been snapped from its base and was drifting loose in the sea. I brought it to shore in a bucket of sea water
to have a close look at its polyps. Several hours later, I was surprise to see two starfish, each no bigger than a fingertip, crawling
about in the bucket. They had made their homes within the stem
of the gorgonian, it seemed, and had come ashore with it!

A not-so-soft soft coral is the alcyonarian known as *organ-
pipe coral*, found in all tropical seas. It is composed of a great
many tubes that stand upright and parallel, bound together by
crosswise platforms, so that the whole colony looks very much
like the pipes of an organ. The tubes of the skeleton are red,

but while the coral is alive the polyps cover it, even in the day-time, and their greenish color is what is seen. Within the hollow tubes all sorts of small creatures take up residence—worms, crabs, snails, sponges, and many others. Though organ-pipe coral is able to build a strong supporting skeleton of lime for itself, its polyps have the eight-tentacled structure that groups them with the alcyonarians.

Another hard-skeletoned alcyonarian is *blue coral,* found in the Pacific. It takes the form of upright clumps of plate-shaped stone a foot or two high. It is dull blue-gray on the outside and a much brighter blue within.

The most famous alcyonarian of all is not found on any coral reef. This is *Corallium,* the beautiful red coral that is used in jewelry. The hard red stone is the central core, which is covered during the coral's life by a soft, barklike crust. The inner core takes a high polish, and for thousands of years has been desired for beads and rings. The Greeks and Romans prized it, and there are several references to its value and beauty in the Bible. This coral grows in cool, deep water, and most of the commercial supply comes from the Mediterranean Sea, the Atlantic Ocean, and the waters off Japan. It has never been found on any of the world's coral reefs. The coral known to jewellers as *black coral* is also an alcyonarian, and likewise is unknown on the reefs.

The madrepores or stony corals and the alcyonarians or soft corals are all placed together in the group of animals known as *anthozoa* ("flower-animals"). They get their name from their waving tentacles, which give the polyps the appearance of small flowers. The anthozoa, in turn, are part of the large animal group known as the coelenterates, as we have already seen. One very common type of coral belongs to a different tribe of the coelenterates—the hydrozoa ("water-animals").

This is the smooth-looking, troublesome coral known as *mille-*

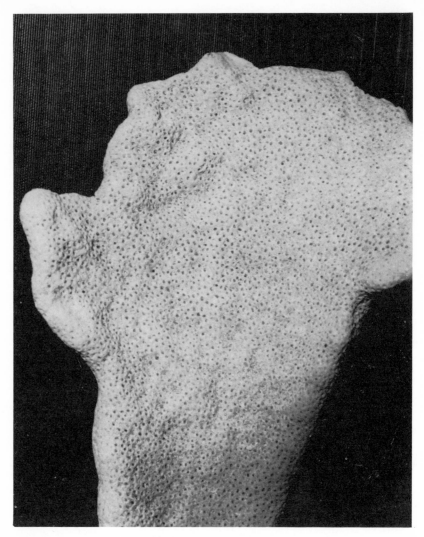

Skeleton of fire coral

pora, better known as fire coral or stinging coral. Most corals of the reef can be touched without fear; the polyps do not like it, but they have no way of fighting back. Fire coral does. All coral polyps have stings that are used on microscopic plankton, but

this one coral can cause a painful skin rash on any large creature foolish enough to touch it—including human beings.

Fire coral is found in every part of the reef, from the shallow
water to the deep. Its color is usually a kind of mustard-brown,
shading into yellow or orange. In shallow water, fire coral grows
as a thin crust spreading over rocks, dead coral, or even living
coral and sponges. Where the water is deeper, it develops great
towers and ramparts, folding in on itself again and again in a
structure of great beauty. Brightly colored fish lurk in the
canyons of the fire coral, many of them unaffected by the stings
for reasons that scientists still do not know.

The texture of fire coral is different from that of the true
corals. There are no ridges, no puckered cups of polyps. A close
look (careful!) shows the surface to be covered with small
blisterlike pores that are nearly invisible except under a magnify-
ing glass. The tentacles of the polyps emerge from these pores,
but they are too small to be seen with the naked eye. The polyps
themselves are much simpler than those of anthozoan corals,
having no mesenteries.

The fire coral's artillery is of two kinds. The tentacles of the
polyps have sharp spines that strike at any disturbing invader.
Also, there are special stinging cells called *nematocysts,* which
contain coiled-up threads of great length. When the polyp is
disturbed, the nematocysts open and the threads whip out to
do their job of stinging. Many a swimmer, buffeted by sudden
rough water or simply in need of a brief rest, has reached out
to grab fire coral with his hand to steady himself. It is a mistake
that few reef-explorers ever make a second time.

The last of our groups of reef-builders are perhaps the most
confusing at all. They are the *nullipores,* which look like coral
and behave like coral—but are not coral at all, or even animals
of any other kind! They are plants which are capable of forming a hard, stony skeleton just as coral polyps do. Early natu-

ralists mistook them for mineral outcroppings; the scientists of the late eighteenth century classed them with the corals, as animals, and not until 1837 were they recognized as plants of the algae group, related to seaweeds.

The nullipores get their name because they do not have visible openings—in contrast with the real corals, which are dotted with the numerous polyp-holding cups. They are of tremendous importance in building coral reefs, because they form an encrusting layer of solid limestone that binds the loose growths of true coral into a single mass. Corals are rigid and often brittle, and tend to break up when hit by high waves; the nullipores thrive in rough water, and through their growth build up a shelter from the sea behind which the corals can flourish. They creep along the edge of the reef, laying down a protecting sheet of stone, forming knolls and banks, spreading from boulder to boulder, cementing everything firmly. Their color ranges from dark red to light pink, and they take many forms, from flat crusts to elaborate branching shapes, dainty and attractive.

These, then, are the builders of the reef: the stony corals and the soft corals, the stinging coral, and the corallike algae. They work together, and the complex interplay of forces gives rise to the enormous bulk of the reef. Boulders and terraces, archways and corridors, towers and domes form the patterns; trembling gorgonians add color and liveliness; encrusting algae contribute splashes of red and pink. An infinity of small creatures draws stone from the sea and builds upward toward the sun, year after year—until vast coral structures, hundreds of feet thick, press down against the ocean floor. No polyp, of course, can suspect that it has contributed to this huge structure. It is aware only of its immediate needs and surroundings. Is the water warm enough? Is the food supply steady? Do the currents keep the sand from piling over the reef? Then the polyp continues to work—and the reef grows and grows and grows.

3.

Dwellers on the Reef

The reef is well populated. Its complicated structure makes it a good home for many kinds of creatures, and they all have their roles in the life and growth of the reef. Since they occupy different zones in the reef vicinity, we can get to know them most easily if we look at them as we would meet them in their own surroundings.

We can begin at the shore. The sea meets the land here, and, though no coral is found living on the beach, many of the smaller reef creatures inhabit it—animals that once were water-dwelling forms, but which now are capable of spending much or even all of their time in the open. As we walk down the beach, we can find many of them, though it often takes keen eyesight to spot them.

The beach itself is a product of the reef. That fine white sand, which feels so good under foot, is made up of powdered coral, beaten into sand by the action of the waves and by other forces, such as the powerful jaws of the creatures that chew coral to feed on polyps. The sand is not entirely made of coral, though; the skeletons of sponges and sea urchins, the shells of clams and snails, the bodies of crabs and lobsters all contribute to the formation of sand. So do the bodies of microscopic one-celled animals called *foraminifera,* whose shells are of limestone, and the remains of the minute plants known as *diatoms,* which live within hard boxes of a glassy substance known as silica. The sand of a tropical beach is made up of all these things, ground to fine grains through the work of wind and water.

As we walk down the beach, ghostly little gray figures scamper rapidly away from us. They are sand crabs, whose homes are in moist burrows three or four feet deep at the water's edge. Most crabs live in water, but the sand crabs are adapted for life on shore; their gills have developed into simple lungs that can breathe air. They are two or three inches broad, and

A crab of the Caribbean shore

their eyes sit atop long movable stalks. Moving lightly on tiptoe over the sand, they scurry sideways, feeding on the stranded plankton creatures that are tossed up by the surf.

Many other kinds of crab live at the shoreline. There are the round, pale blue soldier crabs, which march in huge battalions over the sand, and the fiddler crabs, armed with huge orange front nippers that may be bigger than the entire body of the crab, and the rock crabs, green or brown or blue, moving quickly over the creviced rocks along the shore. The rock crabs are alert and intelligent-looking, and retreat speedily from any hint of danger.

We may see a snail shell walking hurriedly away from us on a host of bright red or blue legs. Snails do not have legs, so we know that what we have seen is a hermit crab. Most crabs have

Hermit crab

hard outer shells, but the hermit crab lacks this armor. To shield his soft belly from harm he uses the discarded shell of a snail as a house, crawling backward into it with only his claws and head visible. Snail shells are coiled in a spiral, and the hermit crab's body is coiled the same way in back, so he fits snugly, hooking himself into the shell so tightly that it is impossible to remove him without damage.

The first job of a newborn hermit crab is to find a shell to live in. Plenty of empty snail shells are available, and anyone who snorkels around offshore rocks in water a couple of feet deep is likely to see hundreds of baby hermit crabs clustered together in shells half an inch long, moving about on tiny feet. As they grow, problems arise. The true crabs, who have shell armor of their own, solve the growth dilemma by moulting: that is, their shells split when they have been outgrown, and the crab crawls out, to live dangerously for a few days until his new shell has hardened. A hermit crab does not grow his own shell, and so his difficulties are much greater. He must abandon his borrowed and outgrown home and find a new one big enough for his needs.

When moving day arrives, the hermit crab is careful not to leave his old home until he has located a bigger shell that looks suitable. He comes forth and quickly stuffs his tender body into the new shell, wriggling and twisting in order to get properly settled. When the process is finished, the hermit crab can relax —until the next time. He must move many times in his life, and if he is lucky he will survive until he is big enough to need the shell of a giant snail such as a conch, which may weigh several pounds. Shell collectors often pluck conchs from the bottom only to find an evil-tempered old hermit crab living inside. Since a big hermit crab's nippers can inflict a nasty wound, it is not a pleasant surprise to come upon one that way.

Here and there on the beach may be some rocks and boulders.

Possibly they were formed when a volcano hurled molten lava down, for many of the coral-fringed islands were once active volcanoes, particularly in the West Indies. Perhaps the boulders are big coral heads, dead brain or star corals that were thrown on shore by tropical storms. One thing is sure: they will be inhabited. Snails of many sorts will be crawling slowly over them, gathering their dinners.

Snails belong to the large group of animals known as *mollusks*. Oysters, clams, scallops, octopuses, squids, and many other creatures are also classed as mollusks. The name comes from a Latin word meaning "soft," for mollusks are soft-bodied, boneless creatures, though most of them are protected by a hard shell. Mollusks such as clams and scallops have two shells or valves, upper and lower, and so are called bivalves. Snails, having only one shell, are univalves.

Snails are widespread animals. They are found on land, living in trees and gardens; at the shore; and in the water. Millions of years ago all snails were water-dwellers, but certain kinds have become adapted to life on land. Among them are the periwinkles, small snails with tapering pointed shells, that can be found on rocks high above the water-line. Periwinkles, though born in the sea, spend much of their time on dry land, and one kind of periwinkle can live on the shore for a month at a time without contact with water. Like all snails, periwinkles have a single foot on which they move slowly around. A rasplike tongue called a *radula* is constantly at work, scraping at the film of microscopic algae that covers the rocks. As they feed, the periwinkles wear down the rocks; one scientist measured a seashore rock for sixteen years and found that in that time the grazing periwinkles had ground it down by three-eighths of an inch!

Closer to the water, other snails will be feeding the same way. The round ones marked with black-and-white checks are the neritas; they must spend more time in water than periwinkles,

Nerita shells—the nickel shows the size

but are not at all troubled when a low tide leaves them stranded out of the water for several hours. Nearby, clinging so tightly to the rocks that they cannot be removed, are the cap-shaped limpets. These little mollusks are univalves also, but their shells are flat, rather than coiled into a spiral as are those of most snails. Not even the fiercest of pounding waves can knock a limpet loose; it stays put, grinding away at the film of algae with its radula.

The same shoreline rocks may be dotted with cone-shaped shells that look something like volcanoes, with sloping sides and "craters" at the summit. These may seem to be limpets or some other mollusk, but actually they are the much more complicated creatures known as *barnacles*. Barnacles belong to the group called *crustaceans*, or shellfish, which includes lobsters, shrimps, and crabs. Newborn barnacles look very much like other new-

Limpet shell

born crustaceans. But after swimming freely for a while, the baby barnacle finds a convenient rock, or perhaps the hull of a boat, and settles down for life. It attaches its head first, and begins to secrete a shell consisting of tightly fitted plates around an opening in the center. As the sea washes the barnacle's rock, bringing a rich haul of plankton creatures, the plates open to allow six pairs of bristle-covered feelers to poke out. These act as a net, snaring the plankton and pulling it into the barnacle's shell to be eaten. The white shells of barnacles accumulate by the thousands along the shoreline rocks, one barnacle often attaching itself right above another. When a questing finger approaches the barnacle, the little crustacean slams the shell-plates closed and waits for the intruder to disappear.

Another member of the shore population is the *chiton*, a mollusk that lives in eroded depressions in the rocks. Chitons are oval-shaped, an inch or two long, with shells divided into

Two neritas (left) and a chiton on a rock

eight sections and held together by tough leathery bands. They
are algae-eaters too, rasping away at the rock; frequently, chitons pile up, one atop the other, and each scrapes algae from
the back of the one beneath it. These unusual mollusks have an
oddly primitive, ancient look, and it is not surprising to learn
that fossil chitons many millions of years old have been discovered, looking not very different from those of today.

Probably the most appealing shoreline mollusk is the sea hare,
a soft, gentle creature of the shallows. Sea hares can be found
in the rocks and weeds of the shore at low tide, but it takes
a keen observer to notice them, for their color provides a near-
perfect camouflage. They are snails who wear their shells inside;
externally, they have soft mantles, tan or greenish-yellow with
dark rings, that surround an incomplete inner shell. Two pairs
of tentacles sprout from the head, and the back pair stands upright in a rabbit-ear position that gives the sea hare its name.
In the West Indies and the Florida Keys, sea hares are usually
three or four inches long, but one species of Australia's Great
Barrier Reef reaches lengths of fifteen inches.

In snail fashion, a sea hare browses on rocks and seaweeds,
moving slowly on his single, sticky foot. If molested, a sea hare
will give off a "smokescreen" of violet-colored liquid, but after
that one burst of irritation, which stains the water around it a
delicate cranberry red, the sea hare becomes placid again. If
gently picked up and held on the palm of the hand, it will
patiently wait to be returned to the water, where it will continue its browsing as though nothing had happened to interrupt
its activities.

As we move from the shore to the shallow water, a new group
of creatures is discovered. There is not usually any coral in the
water just offshore, for the surf keeps the sand stirred up and
coral polyps that land there cannot live. The sandy bottom is

A dead sting ray on the sea bottom, with urchins investigating it

inhabited by a variety of burrowing crabs, clams, and worms, but since these keep out of sight most of the time we will pass them by and continue to slightly deeper water. Here, thick green strands of turtle-grass sprout, and in these meadows a number of animals make their homes.

This is sea-urchin territory. Sea urchins are classed with the animals called *echinoderms,* a name that means "spiny skins." There are hundreds of different kinds of sea urchins. One type that we might have noticed near the shore was the short-spined black rock-boring urchin, living in hollows and crannies in the stone. This urchin, with stubby black spines and a deep red body, tucks itself away in openings hardly bigger than itself, and waits for the water to sweep food toward it.

The most common urchin of the turtle-grass zone is a gray-bodied, white-spined one. This living pincushion camouflages itself by wrapping bits of grass and coral fragments in its spines, and crawls along the bottom, nibbling at shells and coral. Urchins have hundreds of tube-shaped feet that project through holes in the rounded stiff case of the animal. To walk with the tube-feet, the urchin pumps them full of water, which makes them swell, and pushes them in the direction it wants to go. By letting the water out of the feet, the urchin contracts them and pulls itself forward. Underneath the urchin is the mouth opening, with five teeth visible. Within, a complicated mill that has long been known as Aristotle's lantern grinds up the food.

The white-spined sea urchin shows no objections if it is picked up in the hand to be examined; its tube-feet will emerge and wave feebly, but otherwise the urchin will not react. Another harmless urchin is the sluggish slate-pencil urchin, which gets its name from its thick stubby spines. But one urchin that is certainly not to be handled at all is the long-spined black urchin, found almost anywhere in the water around a coral reef. Every rock, every coral clump, every patch of sand or turtle-grass displays the needlelike black quills of this urchin.

The long-spined black urchin is the most dangerous creature of the reef—sharks included. One shark can do a great deal more harm to a swimmer than one sea urchin. But in many years of reef exploration, I have yet to see my first shark, while I have never failed to encounter hundreds of these urchins on every swim. The fragile spines break at a touch, enter the skin, and cause inflammations and infections. The effect of being pricked by a sea-urchin spine is like that of a hornet sting; and since one urchin has dozens of spines, a careless swimmer can find himself in great pain if he accidentally comes in contact with an urchin of this kind. Full-grown ones have bodies about four inches in diameter, and spines a foot long. The spines are in constant motion, and will swing around to point ominously toward a possible enemy. Sea urchins never attack, any more than poison ivy attacks—but they are everywhere in the sea, and alertness is in order at all times.

Also found in the shallows is the starfish, which likewise belongs to the echinoderms. More than 2,000 kinds of starfish are known, found in every ocean and at every depth down to 15,000 feet. The best-known kinds are five-armed and usually red in color, but there are starfish with six, a dozen, and even fifty arms. They range in size from an inch or two in diameter to three feet, fully grown. Most of the starfish seen near coral reefs are about a foot across. During the day, many are hidden under coral boulders, but some remain in the open, conspicuous against the sand or the turtle-grass.

Like sea urchins, starfish walk by filling their tube-feet with water, clamping the swollen feet against something, and letting the water out of the feet to pull themselves forward. Starfish use their tube-feet in another way, too: to force open the shells of the clams and other bivalves that form their chief food. Clams, oysters, and scallops have powerful muscles to keep the two halves of their shells closed, but starfish are even more powerful; they wrap themselves around a bivalve and maintain a steady suction grip until the mollusk tires and lets its shell gape open. A narrow opening is all that the starfish needs. Strange as it sounds, it is able to send its stomach out through its mouth and into the clam or oyster. It digests its prey, leaving the empty shells behind, and pulls its stomach back where it belongs.

Relatives of the starfish are the brittle stars, which few visitors to the reef ever see. They consist of small, round, disk-like bodies to which are attached five thin, long, extremely flexible arms. During the day brittle stars stay hidden under rocks and seaweed. Another unusual starfish rarely seen is the basket

star, a weird creature that looks like a visitor from another
planet. It has five arms, about two feet long, but each of them is
divided into branches, and each of the branches is divided again,
and each of the sub-sub-divisions is divided, on and on until
the basket star becomes a writhing mass of snaky tendrils. In
daytime, it slumps into a tangled heap that looks like a pile of
dead gorgonians, but after dark the lacy arms unfold and the
finely branched armlets reach out to snare particles of food.

Mollusks are present in the shallow-water zone too. Many
snails live here, including such part-time water-dwellers as the
periwinkles and neritas. The monarch of all snails is found here,
the magnificent conch, with its thick, heavy, many-knobbed shell.
Conchs may weigh five pounds or more, and have shells a foot

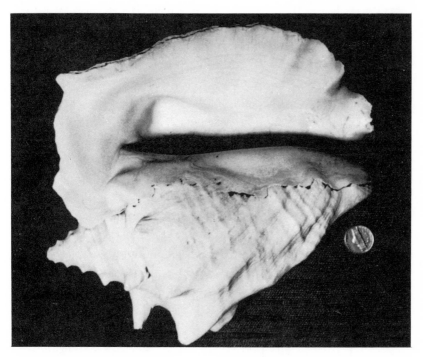

Conch shell—the nickel shows its size

long and six to eight inches high. Usually the outside of the shell is a dull gray in color, and its inner surface is richly tinted with yellows, pinks, and deep orange-browns. Its big inhabitant has large, keen eyes, which stare indignantly at snorkelers who pass overhead. If the shell is picked up, the conch immediately pulls out of sight. As is true of all snails, it has a horny appendage called an *operculum*, which serves as a "door" to barricade the shell. The operculum of most snails is simply a flat plate, but a conch's has a clawlike appearance, and the conch uses it in getting about, digging the tip of the operculum into the sand and tugging itself forward. A disturbed conch can travel quickly in this manner, flopping awkwardly from side to side as it moves, but usually it prefers to pull into its shell and wait for trouble to go away. If the trouble is human, it usually does not go away, for conch meat is considered a seafood delicacy in the tropics, and the handsome shells are used as ornaments and for jewelry. Though thousands of conchs are captured each year, the large mollusks still remain common in the turtle-grass shallows.

Another reef mollusk, not found in Caribbean waters, is the cone shell, the only snail dangerous to man. This pretty shell, three to four inches long and decorated with wavy stripes, is common on Australian reefs. It possesses a fleshy projection that is armed with sharp spines. Poison glands are located at the base of each spine. If the cone shell is handled, it will strike out with its spines, and the poison will cause severe pain and temporary paralysis. Several cases have been recorded of shell collectors who died as a result of cone-shell stings.

Australia's reefs also are inhabited by the famous and dangerous giant clam, *Tridacna gigas*. Many adventure stories tell of divers or swimmers who accidentally thrust an arm or a leg into the shell of this huge clam and are caught in an unbreakable grip, drowning before help can reach them. Though not all adventure tales are true, stories about this clam can be believed.

Giant *Tridacnas* are plentiful on the Australian reefs; they sit
with the hinge side down and their shell-opening uppermost,
their valves apart so that food-bearing water can flow through.
Some are four and five feet long, with shells that weigh hundreds
of pounds. When the shells are open, a velvety mantle of flesh is
visible, usually brown or green with dark markings and bright
green spots. Since the clams usually live in crevices between
masses of coral, someone walking over the reef at low tide can
easily step on this mantle and slide within the great shells, which
instantly clamp as tight as a vise. It is impossible to pry the
shells apart with bare hands alone. The only way to do it is to
insert something sharp, such as a crowbar or a long knife,
between the shells, cutting the clam's powerful muscle. Few visitors to the reefs carry crowbars, and so there have been many
instances when fishermen or shell-gatherers, trapped within a
giant clam, have drowned when the tides rose.

The danger of being caught by one of these monsters of the
mollusk tribe has been greatly exaggerated, though. Most of the
big *Tridacnas* grow in isolated places, and their size and colorful
mantles make them about as hard to overlook as a mailbox on the
reef would be. At low tide, they make themselves even more
conspicuous by squirting columns of water many feet into the air
to clear their tissues of accumulated silt and wastes. It is possible
to locate the giant clams on the reef simply by watching for these
spouting geysers.

Many smaller *Tridacna* clams are found on Pacific reefs. What
they lack in size, they make up in beauty. Dr. Paul A. Zahl,
an American naturalist who spent several months on Australia's
reefs in 1955, wrote that when these smaller clams are "observed
through several inches of the reef's window-clear water, valves
gaping and mantle tissues exposed, they are one of nature's love-
liest sights and a dye mixer's dream. No two are the same. The
mantle of one will be electric blue, another just as intensely

green, or yellow, mauve, or orange, with these colors in infinite combination, and mottled, striped, and speckled in every conceivable design."

Clams do not have true eyes, but they have light-sensitive organs that allow them to detect the shadows of enemies, and they shut tight at the slightest hint of trouble. The bivalve mollusks called scallops have extremely good eyes, dozens of them mounted along the rim of the mantle. Scallops have an even more unusual feature: practically alone among the bivalves, they are able to "swim." They do it by clapping their valves together rapidly, causing water to spurt out at the sides of the shells. This gives the scallop an oddly jerky motion; it shoots through the water in clumsy zigs and zags, doing a wild dance that carries it away from danger with surprising speed.

As we get beyond the region of sand and turtle-grass, and into the area where the first small clumps of coral appear, different reef creatures come into view, living on, in, or under the coral. Living things are everywhere, and a single coral head a few feet across may shelter a host of animals. The spiny black sea urchins are here, sometimes in clusters of fifteen or twenty, sometimes occupying a coral cranny in solitary prickliness. Gorgonians add to the density of the coral "jungle," making fine homes for seagoing crabs and snails.

The bivalves are represented by forms that drill their way right into the coral to live. Burrowing clams, found on reefs in all parts of the world, are free-swimming animals when they are born. Then they alight on a crack or depression in dead coral and attach themselves to the stone with tough, sticky threads. Next, they rock to and fro against the coral, patiently wearing it away to create niches for themselves. They are less than half an inch long when they begin this process, and by the time they have reached the size of an inch, they have burrowed so deeply

A sea urchin living in a hollow of a brain coral

into the rock that they lie flush with its surface. As they grow, they continue to bore into the coral, endlessly rocking to enlarge their living quarters. In Australia these clams reach a maximum size of about six inches.

Another driller is the date mussel, which uses acid to make its tunnels. Clinging to dead coral, it gives off a chemical that breaks down the calcium carbonate of the rock. The chemical would dissolve the shell of the mussel too, since it is also made of calcium carbonate, were it not covered with a protective layer of a horny material. These mussels create holes an inch wide and four to five inches deep.

Burrowing clams and date mussels are reef-destroying agents. They undo the work of the coral polyps, grinding rock to sand as they make their way inward. When they die, they contribute their limy shells to the reef, but that does not balance the damage they do. Their tunnels weaken the coral so that it can be broken free by storms.

Other creatures honeycomb the coral with tunnels too. The tubeworms are the most common of these. They are of many kinds, and their brightly colored, flowery-looking gills provide spots of lively hue on the reef. Some tubeworms bore into living coral; others fashion tubes of sand or shells glued together with mucus, and live attached to the coral without harming it. They

Tubeworm

rarely, if ever, leave their burrows. Their handsome plumes, feathery and delicate, flutter in the water beyond the edge of the tube, bringing oxygen and food to the hidden worm. Wave a flipper at a cluster of tubeworms and they vanish instantly, ducking out of sight until trouble passes.

A different sort of worm can be seen crawling over the rocks or in and out of empty snail shells. These are the *nereids,* or bristleworms, which look like flat green-and-brown ribbons an inch wide and five or six inches long. They have well-developed jaws, and feed on small crustaceans and worms. I have seen a nereid at work devouring a much larger sea urchin, which waved its long spines helplessly as the nereid gnawed at its body. Nereids are armed with bundles of horny bristles along their sides; they are sharp and break off easily, working their way into the skin of anyone rash enough to handle one of these worms. The zoologist T. C. Roughley tells the story of the time he picked up a nereid in his gloved hand, on a reef off the coast of New South Wales, Australia. "Taking off my glove," he writes, "I found hundreds of fine white spines embedded in the tip of my index finger; the leather glove had offered no resistance to them at all. If there is anything in the world sharper than the bristles of this worm I should like to see it, but please hand it to me on a plate. The tip of my finger remained partially numbed for six weeks afterwards."

The *palolo,* a worm of this family found in the South Pacific, is responsible for a strange and beautiful spectacle each year. This worm lives in burrows in dead coral. It hides from the light of day; even moonlight seems to bother it, and it emerges from its cave to feed only late at night. It grows until it reaches a length of five to eight inches.

As the spawning season approaches, a mysterious change comes over the palolo. The rearmost third of its body begins to swell as egg cells or sperm cells develop. The females take on a gray-green color in this part of their bodies, while the males become deep pink. On a single night, the palolos thrust these swollen hind parts out of their hiding places. They begin to writhe and twist—and break loose. By the millions, the parts of the worms that carry the sex cells swim toward the surface, while the cave-dwelling part of the worm goes back to its timid life in the darkness under the sea.

Dawn finds an uncountable number of these severed palolo tails swimming in the water around the reef. As the sun rises, they start a weird dance, the greenish female fragments and the pink males quivering and straining until they burst. Sperm cells and egg cells pour forth, turning the water a milky color, and the new palolos are conceived. The empty skins of the tail segments sink to the bottom to decay, and the young palolos begin to develop, while in the depths the old worms grow their missing parts anew in preparation for next year's mating season.

The palolo spawning takes place at the same time each year on every reef. On the Pacific island of Samoa, where scientists first studied this phenomenon in 1857, the palolos spawn exactly one week after the November full moon. It is a time of rejoicing for the natives; they value the worms for food, and when the water begins to churn with its burden of green and pink worms the Samoans come forth, gathering them in buckets. They hold a great feast, which must last them until the following year.

Palolos are also found in the Caribbean and Atlantic. On the reefs of the Dry Tortugas, off Florida, spawning takes place during the last quarter of the July moon. The palolos of the West Indies are luminous, giving off bright flashes of light as they writhe in the sea. When Christopher Columbus neared land on the night of October 11, 1492, he saw a mysterious glow "about four hours before making the landfall and an hour before moon-rise," and it has been suggested that he was witnessing the spawning of the palolos off the Bahamas.

Few of the northerners who visit the tropical reefs are lucky enough to arrive in time to see the palolos. But any alert snorkeler can enjoy another beautiful form of reef life: the sea anemones, the "flowers of the reef."

Sea anemones are animals. They are classed with the coelenterates, and both the sea anemones and the coral polyps are in the anthozoa group ("flower-animals"). Anemones do not secrete limestone, and they are much bigger than individual coral polyps; but their structure is basically the same: a hollow tube with a mouth and tentacles at one end.

The tentacles give the sea anemones their name. They are thick and fleshy, almost like the petals of a flower. Often they are the only part of the anemone that is visible, for the sturdy tubular body is usually hidden in the sand. The lovely petals wave enticingly, and any small animal that approaches will find their beauty a deadly snare, for stinging cells wait to paralyze and capture anything edible.

Sea anemones are found in many parts of the world, not only on coral reefs. They have a variety of forms; some of them are an inch or two across, others a foot or more. There are anemones with short stubby tentacles half an inch long, and anemones whose tentacles stretch out six inches. The bigger ones are usually drab in color, grayish-green or brown, but small anemones can be brilliant in hue. On the Great Barrier Reef, where everything is improbably large, one type of anemone reaches giant size. Dr. Paul Zahl describes it: "The creature, clinging to the side of a small pool, was a full twenty inches across, with its surface comprising a veritable forest of olive-green tentacles all writhing, swaying, expanding, and contracting like the serpents on the head of a Gorgon." These big anemones feed on crabs, shrimp, and even small fish.

It seems astonishing, then, to learn that certain crabs, shrimp, and fish live right within reach of the anemone's tentacles and

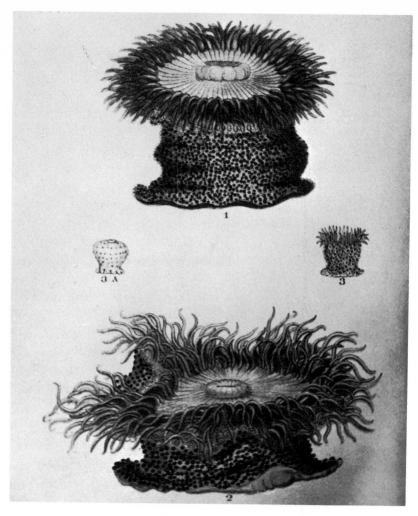

Sea anemones and their young—from Dana's *Corals and
Coral Islands* (1872)

are unharmed by its stinging cells. The fish are brightly colored,
two or three inches long; they snuggle into the tentacles, hiding
in their folds, and even venture into the anemone's stomach at
times. The shrimp and crabs that are associated with giant anemo-

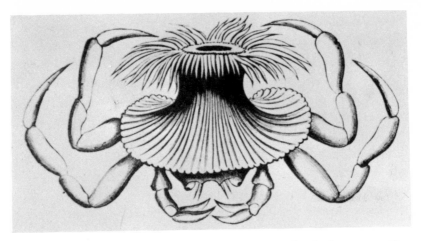

A crab carrying a stinging sea anemone on its back for protection
—from Dana's *Corals and Coral Islands* (1872)

nes are usually transparent and nearly invisible, but occasionally they, too, are bright in color. Sheltered by the stinging tentacles of the anemone, these little creatures do not have to fear attack from their natural enemies. Scientists think they serve their hosts as scavengers, cleaning away the bones and waste materials of the fish the anemone eats. Why they are immune to the stings remains a mystery.

Another odd partnership involves crabs and anemones. One kind of big hermit crab allows small stinging anemones to attach themselves to the outside of its shell. Seven or eight anemones may ride the same shell, serving as a battery of living machine-guns for the crab. Their stinging cells ward off the crab's enemies, while the anemones benefit by eating discarded scraps of the crab's meals. When the time comes for the hermit crab to move to a larger shell, he takes his anemones with him, carefully detaching them with his claws and transferring them to the new shell. The anemones permit this, making no attempt to sting the crab.

In the Indian Ocean, one deep-sea crab carries a luminous anemone on its back as a torch to light the way. The strangest of all these crab-anemone partnerships, though, links a hermit crab of Hawaii's reefs with a small stinging anemone. The crab carries one anemone in each of its two front claws, hardly ever releasing it. In time of danger, the crab waves the anemones in the face of its foes, keeping them back with the stings. At mealtime, the crab uses the anemones as hunting weapons, touching them to small creatures to stun or kill them. The crab uses its second pair of nippers to pull the food apart and carry it to its mouth, and the anemones dine on the leftovers.

Anemones, unlike coral polyps, are usually able to move from place to place. Generally, they remain rooted to the same spot for weeks or months, though they may creep slowly away in search of more favorable quarters. Anemones are extremely long-lived; some anemones in captivity were still alive after seventy-four years. Most of the anemones found on West Indian reefs are unable to sting hard enough to inconvenience a human being, but it's a good idea to avoid handling them anyway, since a few are not so harmless.

As lumpish and unattractive as the anemones are lovely is the *sea cucumber,* found on coral reefs throughout the world. This not very handsome animal is known by various names: the French call it *bêche-de-mer,* or "sea worm"; in Asia it goes under its Malayan name of *trepang.* Sea cucumbers are sausage-shaped creatures that range in length from a few inches to several feet. They lie seemingly lifeless on the sand flats, among the coral, and near the shore, and hardly move at all. They are usually some dark, drab color, although yellow and white ones are known, and on the Great Barrier Reef one species is bright crimson below and jet black above.

Sea cucumbers are echinoderms, relatives of the starfish and sea urchin. Despite their name ("spiny-skinned"), their skins do not have spines—the skins may be thick and leathery, or soft and faintly slimy. They crawl unhurriedly along the bottom on tube-feet that are instantly pulled in when the animal is lifted from the water for inspection. At one end is a mouth, fringed with sticky tentacles, and at the other end is the anus, for disposal of waste matter. The sea cucumber drags sand in through its mouth, filters any food material from it, and excretes it at the anus. Since it spends all its time at this process, tons of sand pass through a sea cucumber every year.

Its cousin, the starfish, has a curious method of dealing with enemy attack. It can break off one or more of its own arms, leaving them to be devoured while it crawls off to safety. Later, the starfish is able to grow back the severed arms. The sea cucumber, which has no arms to sacrifice in this way, has an even more startling method for meeting attack: it hurls its internal organs out of its body! With a quick contraction of its muscles it spews its stomach forth and leaves it behind while escaping. Within a week or so, the sea cucumber grows a new set of organs and is apparently unharmed by its experience.

When a sea cucumber empties its insides, it also evicts a tenant. Many sea cucumbers are inhabited by one or more of the slender, eel-like fish called the pearl fish or *Fierasfer*, which live within the animal's stomach unharmed by its digestive juices. In his book, *The Living Sea*, undersea explorer Jacques-Yves Cousteau tells how a member of his team of divers found a big sea cucumber "and was holding it up for a photograph when the sea cucumber emptied itself. The organs fell out and with them two slender living fish about a foot long, which wriggled desperately on deck. . . . They had not been eaten by the sea cucumber, but were its associates, called pearl fish, who find hospitality in the intestine of the cucumber."

While exploring the sea bottom with Aqualung equipment, Captain Cousteau "observed the curious method by which a frightened pearl fish retreats inside the cucumber. It does not enter the mouth. The pearl fish places its tail in the anus of the host and wiggles in backwards. The sea cucumber gets its food by sucking in sand and filtering out minute organisms. This thin gruel did not seem adequate to feed one or two active fish as well. We thought that the pearl fish must spend most of the day in the cucumber and go out at night to make its living."

The sea cucumber has few natural enemies, and does not have to perform its stomach-ejecting trick often. The big fish of the reef show little interest in eating sea cucumbers. The worst threat to the sea cucumber is the Chinese appetite. The Chinese, who have had three thousand years to invent every conceivable kind of dish, make a soup from sea cucumbers that gourmets value highly. Every year hundreds of tons of the creatures are caught off the Australian coasts and shipped to Hong Kong for distribution to the chefs of China.

Of all the animals of the reef, the ones that look and behave least like animals are the sponges. Sponges abound on the reef, growing on and under the coral, or on the sand, or over rocks like a crust. The long red or purple tubes of one kind of sponge stretch upward from the bottom; big gray-black sponges that look like rubbery wastebaskets sit in solitary splendor; yellow and brown and green and white sponges of varying forms sprout in great numbers. Their range in size is from a fraction of an inch to several yards across.

Sponges are extremely primitive animals—so primitive that for centuries they were considered to be plants. Aristotle, the best scientific observer of the ancient world, said that sponges were animals, but this was long thought to be one of that sage's errors of judgment. A man named John Ellis made a close study of sponges in 1765, noticing how water currents were pulled through them by the action of parts of their bodies, and realized that Aristotle had been right.

A sponge consists of a loose grouping of cells. There are no organs in any understandable sense of the word: no stomach, no gills, no nervous system, certainly no brain. The body form may vary, but there is always a central cavity lined with cells that have active, whiplike cilia. These tiny whips beat constantly, drawing water into the sponge's body through the thousands of small pores that dot its skin. The water carries food and oxygen, which the sponge uses for its life processes. After the water has passed through the sponge's body and is no longer of value, it passes out again through a large central opening, the *osculum*. A thin layer of outer cells forms a skin for the sponge; between the skin and the inner whip-bearing cells, there is a layer of jellylike substance and a skeletal framework.

The sponge's skeleton is what is used for bath sponges. In those that are marketed for bath sponges, the skeleton is composed of a horny substance called *spongin*. Other sponges have skeletons of calcium carbonate, which makes them nearly as hard as coral, while a third group has skeletons of glasslike silicon. These glassy sponges are often quite beautiful, but their sharp, brittle fibers make them useless for bathing or washing.

Though a sponge seen on the reef appears to be absolutely motionless, it is actually working hard all the time. The unseen inner cilia never rest in the labor of drawing water into the sponge. A sponge only four inches high must filter twenty-five gallons of water a day. In order to take in enough food to gain an ounce, a sponge must draw a ton of water through its body.

Like coral polyps, sponges have a free-swimming stage before they settle down. They reproduce sexually, and the newborn sponges swim until they come to rest on a suitable place. Then they attach themselves and begin to grow. Sponges can also reproduce asexually, by budding. As a further indication of how simple they are in the pattern of animal development, sponges can be cut to pieces and will grow into new complete individuals.

On the sponge "farms" of the West Indies, bath sponges are grown by cutting large sponges into pieces a few inches long, which then develop into many full-sized sponges. The commercial sponge industry has been badly hurt by the competition of plastics, and nearly all the bath sponges sold in the United States today are synthetic.

Sponges are found in all seas and all climates. The tropical sponges of the coral seas are of many varieties. The flexible tube-shaped sponges are seen commonly on the reef. The lovely deep-blue sponge called the azure vase is found in the West Indies; it reaches heights of nearly a foot. Off the big island

**Loggerhead sponge encrusted with fire coral (left) ;
tube sponges (right)**

of Jamaica, one can sometimes see the fringed basket sponge, whose red body has an eight-inch central opening. And an impressive sight of tropical waters is the charcoal-colored loggerhead sponge, which can reach the size and shape of a large barrel.

Loggerhead sponges, containing hundreds of intricate passageways, serve as "apartment houses" for many small creatures. The crustacean known as the snapping shrimp is a permanent lodger; its young, floating on the tides, enter the loggerhead sponge and make their homes in the inner passages, scraping food from the walls of the sponge until they grow too big to escape. When new shrimps hatch, they pass out through the openings of the sponge and drift until they find some new one where they can begin the cycle again. Worms, crabs, and other small animals also live in these sponges. A scientist once counted 17,128 animals dwelling within a single big loggerhead sponge. Most of them were shrimps, but there were a number of fish up to five inches long. The sponge does not appear to get any benefit from this arrangement, though it is certainly convenient for the residents.

Sponges and tubeworms, snails and clams, starfish and urchins —all add to the growing reef. Their shells and skeletons accumulate, cemented together by the action of the hard algae. And so the reef grows, a complex and colorful community of many forms of life.

4.

Swimmers and Hunters

The world of the coral reef has other inhabitants, more lively than the sponges and worms and clams. A host of fish flit through the caverns, grottoes, knolls, and byways of the reef. Some prefer the surging, pounding fury of the rough water near the surface; some hide in the shelter of the great coral heads on the bottom; some dwell in the sandy or grassy shallows. This range of surroundings has given rise to fish of every shape and color. A visit to the reef world leaves one dazzled by the splendor and beauty of the coral fish.

Why are they so colorful? Why the riot of reds and greens and yellows and blues? The bold, brilliant colors of the reef fish defy explanation. Nowhere else in the sea is such a rainbow palette employed. Perhaps here in the complex channels of the reef fish do not need camouflage, and can dare to wear gaudy colors, since shelter is always near. But that is not a good enough answer. Some mysterious miracle of nature produced the flamboyant colors of the reef fish, and no really convincing theory has yet been put forth to explain it.

Most of the coral fish are small. A fish more than a foot long is an unusual sight on the reef in daytime, though an occasional big grouper four or five feet long can be spotted, and at night the large deep-water hunters like the shark and barracuda arrive. The typical reef fish are six to twelve inches long, with compact, narrow bodies. They have broad tails and stubby fins, generally, to allow them to make sudden stops and starts and quick turns. The jagged coral thrusts forth a million daggers, and a fish of the reef must be able to maneuver agilely and alertly. In the densely populated reef world, too, enemies are numerous, and a fish must move quickly to survive.

Fish anywhere, but particularly on the reef, are remarkably well engineered for their environment. Water is hundreds of times as dense as air, yet streamlined fish slice through it effortlessly at high speeds. Within most fish is a gas-filled bladder that allows them to hover; adjusting the gas content of the bladder lets them move up or down in the sea. To swim, a fish points its head in the direction it wants to go, and ripples its body. The fins provide balance and steering, and serve as brakes. Fish move quickly; some have been clocked at fifty miles an hour. As we swim over the reef, we will see slow-moving loafers turn on a furious display of speed when the need arises.

We could fill volumes with descriptions of the fish of the reef. With every cranny and cavern the home of dozens of finny ones, their number and variety stun the mind. Here are the queen angelfish, its flat, upright form regally cloaked in blues, golds, and scarlets, and its more somber cousin, the French angelfish, black with bright yellow stripes. Here are squirrelfish, red with white stripes and huge, black-rimmed eyes, clustering timidly at the base of a big coral boulder. Spadefish, silver with black stripes; the sergeant majors, briskly military with black-banded yellow bodies; the sleekly slender blue tangs; the triggerfish, with blue-striped faces—all wheel and dart through the coral caverns. On the green bulk of a brain coral rests a neon goby, two inches long, its slim body a flash of shimmering blue framed in black. All shapes, all colors—nature is generous here.

Some of the fish do bear camouflage even in their brightness. The four-eyed butterfly fish is an example. This small, flattened fish seems to be swimming backward, for its pale body is marked, near its tail, with a big dark spot that looks like a large staring eye. An attacking fish would normally strike at the eye, expecting to seize the butterfly fish by the head; but the butterfly fish, swimming forward, eludes the confused attacker that has lunged at the wrong end of its prey.

Other fish, hiding in the sand between the coral growths, shun bright colors. The sand flounder, for instance, wears a mottled gray skin that allows it to blend perfectly with its surroundings. Completely flat, with both its eyes on the same side of its body, it lies motionless on the bottom, overlooked by everyone.

The long, gray-and-white-speckled lizardfish occupies the same territory. Another bottom-sitter, this fish sits still, confident of its near-invisibility, even while snorkelers approach within a few feet. Then, alarmed at last, it darts away, settling to the bottom again nearby.

Always a sinister sight is a third bottom-dweller, the sting ray. Basically a harmless creature, this relative of the shark drifts through the sand, feeding on clams and other hard-shelled mollusks, which it crushes with broad, flat teeth. When bothered, the sting ray flaps its wing-shaped fins and takes off, skimming a few inches above the bottom as it flees. But a wicked, poisonous spine is mounted on the sting ray's long, tapering tail. An unsuspecting wader who catches an equally unsuspecting sting ray by surprise and steps on that tail will receive an agonizing wound.

Luckily, cases of sting-ray injury are rare. Usually the ray makes its escape before any damage is done, at least in tropical

Sting ray in motion, with a smaller fish swimming just above its back

seas, where the transparent water makes such accidental encounters unlikely. In the murkier waters of northern seas, sting
rays are much more dangerous. One famous victim was Captain
John Smith, who suffered a painful wound while fishing in the
bay near his settlement at Jamestown, Virginia.

Sting rays are generally three or four feet across. Their odd flapping motion and ugly reputation make them chilling creatures to see, despite their timidity. Even more terrifying—though totally harmless—is the giant devil ray, or *manta*, found in the deeper waters surrounding many coral reefs. This jumbo of the ray family has a wingspread of fifteen feet or more, and can weigh several tons. Two hornlike fins jut upward from the head, adding to the devilish appearance. This vast ray, for all its size and nightmarish look, is not armed even with a sting. It feeds on minute animal life, which it sucks in through small, strainerlike teeth. From a deep-sea fishing boat, devil rays can be seen at considerable distances, huge triangular dark shapes in the clear water, the tips of their "wings" knifing through the surface as they swim.

Another camouflaged fish—and this one an utter horror—is the stonefish of the Pacific reefs. C. M. Yonge, who led an important scientific expedition to the Great Barrier Reef in 1928-29, writes that "this fish . . . may fairly lay claim to be the most hideous of living creatures." He talks of its "flabby, unwholesome wartiness and the blotched coloring of gray and green." Another zoologist, T. C. Roughley, tells us that "its body, soft and slimy, is just a mass of horrible warty excrescences; its great upwardly-directed mouth is a sickly green inside; its movements are sluggish and altogether lacking the grace of other fish. Its repulsiveness is complete."

Even these words fail to do justice to the spectacular ugliness of the stonefish. The rough texture of its skin, the blotchy coloring, and its tiny eyes help to make it indistinguishable from the coral and seaweed where it lies in wait. It seems to be just another piece of coral itself, pitted and eroded, covered with bits of seaweed and splotches of sponge. But let some hapless crab or small fish come within reach and the huge mouth opens suddenly in an abrupt, sickening gulp.

There is only one beautiful aspect to the stonefish. Along its back are thirteen spines, a lovely light blue in color. Their beauty masks their frightfulness, for at the base of each of these sharp, steely spines are two poison sacs. The slightest pressure on the spines forces the poison out. Any animal that molests a stonefish instantly receives a fatal dose of venom. Human beings who walk barefoot or in thin sandals over a Pacific reef run the risk of stepping on a stonefish, for the creature never flees from trouble, but remains motionless and concealed, confident of the power of its poison. Many people have died as a result of treading on a stonefish; those who survive undergo months of such intense pain that the victim must be kept in a drugged sleep much of the time.

The Chinese, so we are told, find the flesh of the stonefish good to eat. Perhaps it is; few westerners have cared to experiment with it.

Another fish of the Pacific reefs, as interesting as the stonefish and a good deal less horrifying, is the curious mudskipper, or walking fish, which lives close to shore. At low tide, most shore-dwelling fish move out to sea, but not this one. It basks happily in the sun, and grubs about in the muddy flats where the mangrove trees grow.

The mudskipper is a fish that seems to be evolving toward an existence on land. It will drown if kept under water for any great length of time. About ten inches long, colored a greenish-brown that matches the mud where it is usually found, it can be seen pushing itself along over the mud flats on its thick, fleshy side fins, and even climbing a foot or two up the mangrove trees. If frightened, it will use its fins to skip across the mud to safety at a great speed. It can also use its fins to skip across the surface of water, without submerging. Its favorite foods are insects and small crabs, which it captures by lunging at them.

The mudskipper's body has not only gills but an air cavity

that amounts to a primitive lung. It is able to absorb oxygen from the air through this cavity, as well as to take it in through the gills in the manner of ordinary fish. Frequently, a mud-skipper can be seen lying at the edge of ocean pools with its tail in the water—another way this fish has of breathing. The tail has a thin outer skin that permits oxygen dissolved in the water to pass through and enter the small blood vessels just beneath its surface. In effect, the mudskipper can breathe through its tail!

Another fish with odd habits is the razor fish, found in the Caribbean. This one builds "castles" for itself out of bits of dead coral. These sharp-snouted fish put together structures made up of as many as a thousand pieces of coral, and burrow into them at night. One scientist who studied these fish wrote, "I have long strongly suspected that they return to the same spot habitually to hide, but I did not know that they fence their retreats and maintain property rights in them. They are keen, I find, to keep their piles in order. Every stone I topple into the crater is promptly drawn out and put in place again, which is, after all, not surprising, for the material a single fish gathers may fill an ordinary pail. . . . The capital investment is too great to be abandoned lightly."

Even cleverer architects are the small, beady-eyed, golden and blue fish called *Gnathypops*, which dig vertical, stone-lined burrows in sandy reef floors. Each fish has its own burrow, though they cluster together in "villages." During the day, they remain at home, ceaselessly remodeling and improving their dwellings by diving to the foot of the shaft and coming up to spurt out a mouthful of sand. When feeding time comes, they poke their noses out of the burrows, and, if the coast seems clear, they edge cautiously into view and scout the sea floor for food. Often they pull pieces of dead coral across the mouths of their tunnels to block the entrances while they are gone.

Gnathypops, in its burrow, lives gazing upward while resting on the tip of its tail. Conversely, the boxfish or trunkfish spends much of its time standing on its head. This curious-looking creature, about six inches long, has a square, bony box-shaped "shell" of a mottled-brown or black and white color. Only the tail and fins are free to move. Unable to swivel its head in any direction, the boxfish must tip its entire body downward to graze on the bottom. Encased in its inflexible armor, it moves in solemn dignity, like an old-time banker or broker in his stiffly starched high collar. A close relative, the cowfish, is similar in appearance, but has a pair of small, blunt horns on its forehead.

A common decoration in hotels and restaurants of the tropics is a lamp made by placing a bulb within the dried body of a balloon fish, or blowfish. In life, this gray-green fish has a flat figure and a large head, and can be seen poking around shallow waters nibbling at the coral. It swims slowly and can be caught with the bare hands. When caught, it changes shape amazingly, beginning to inflate like a balloon, and stopping only when it is almost completely round. Short spines emerge and project all over the skin. The balloon fish remains inflated for a few minutes, floating belly upward in the water, as though trying to fool its foes into thinking it is dead. Then it gradually deflates. In the Pacific, fish of this sort are known as toadfish or porcupine fish, and their flesh is considered poisonous.

Many of the reef fish nourish themselves by feeding on the coral polyps. To do this, they are equipped with sharp, strong beaks and special grinders. They pulverize chunks of coral, swallow and digest the polyps, and excrete sand. These fish are active beach-building agents: each year they transform hundreds of pounds of coral into sand.

One of the largest of these reef-munchers is the bumpfish, *Bolbometron,* of the Red Sea. Jacques-Yves Cousteau, writing of a school of bumpfish, said, "Imagine a flat fish four feet long,

weighing more than sixty pounds, with powerful fins, a heavy
jaw equipped with a parrot beak instead of a mouth, and on its
forehead a white bump as prominent as Cyrano's nose—and you
may approximate our surprise upon seeing the bumpfish. They
swam to us in a flock of fifteen head and circled around, flashing
blue-green and orange sides and looking at us with grave eyes."

Captain Cousteau witnessed the bumpfish butting vigorously
against the coral, knocking chunks loose and chewing them.
"The sea bison moved through the stone pasture, grazing with
heavy strokes of the head and sharp cuts of the beak. We could
hear them pulverizing the coral like rock-crushing machines. . . .
A bumpfish must consume several tons of coral a year. The
sparsity of living matter in the coral heads means that they have
to work remarkably hard to survive."

Equally determined coral-chewers are the parrotfish, found
in great numbers in West Indian waters. These are handsome
fish, more than a foot long, with attractive bodies colored deep
turquoise and pink. Armed with a chisel-sharp beak of fused
teeth, the parrotfish scrapes away at the reef all day. The beak is
outlined in deep green, and gives the fish an oddly clownlike
smirk. When darkness falls, the parrotfish often secretes a
transparent sleeping-bag of mucus that forms a complete wrapper
for itself. Or it may simply wedge itself tightly between two
pieces of coral to sleep. Since fish have no eyelids, they can never
close their eyes, but many of them do sleep all the same, and
can be picked up and handled without showing alarm. The
wrasse, a relative of the parrotfish, lies on the bottom and covers
itself with sand when it sleeps. Other fish, such as the flying fish,
never seem to sleep at all. This restless creature, whose fins
spread out to take the form of wings, does not actually fly. It
launches itself through the water, using its tail as a propeller,
until it breaks the surface and goes gliding in the air for distances
up to 150 feet.

Parrotfish

The needlefish, which is related to the flying fish, often is un-noticed by many snorkelers because it swims so close to the surface. With their heads down and their eyes directed toward the bottom, they fail to see this slim, graceful, silvery fish as it glides along six inches or so beneath the waves. Needlefish close to shore are usually about a foot long, but they grow much bigger at sea, and a school of panicky needlefish can cause problems for fishermen in open boats. The big ones, with sharp, long beaks, leap from the water like living javelins, and in their confusion will jump across a boat while its occupants duck for cover.

These bigger needlefish are rarely met on the reef. Also uncommon are the deep-sea killers, the shark and the barracuda.
Though they will enter the reef zone under cover of dark to
feed, these fearsome beasts tend to avoid the narrow channels of
the coral world, and remain in the deeper, bluer waters beyond
the reef.

The barracuda is probably the most evil-looking of fish. Its
gleaming cigar-shaped body is designed for the greatest possible speed and power, and its toothy, underslung jaw is a
menacing sight. Big barracudas, four to six feet long, are
common in the deep water; specimens a foot or two in length
are often seen lurking around the reef. The barracuda is a flesh-
eating fish, but human meat does not often attract it. It is thought
to strike at humans only when extremely hungry, when provoked,
or when in a particularly vicious mood. It has sharp eyes, and
is attracted by bright objects, such as a ring reflecting the flash
of sunlight through the water. The bite of a barracuda is clean
and straight, and even when it does strike its attack is not likely
to be fatal. Fewer than a dozen deaths have been recorded in the
West Indies in the past fifty years from known barracuda attacks. Its reputation, then, is much worse than it deserves to be—
though swimmers certainly find it unnerving to be followed by an
inquisitive, beady-eyed barracuda. They have a habit of doing
that, even when they do not mean to attack.

The shark is much more to be feared. There are 250 species
of shark, ranging in size from one foot to about sixty feet.
Neither the small sharks nor the extremely big ones are dangerous to man, but there are about thirty species of killer sharks,
from five to twenty-five feet in length. Many of the deadly ones,
such as the tiger shark, the great white shark, and the hammer-
head shark, are found in tropical waters.

Sharks are dangerous because they are powerful, because
they are fond of fresh meat, and because they are totally un-

predictable. As Jacques-Yves Cousteau, who has had more than his share of experience with sharks, puts it, "The better acquainted we become with sharks, the less we know them; and one can never tell what a shark is going to do." A big shark may enter waters where people are swimming, glide about on an inspection tour for a while, and leave without doing harm. Or a shark may arrive and begin a savage and often fatal attack on a swimmer without warning or provocation.

It is unwise to brush aside the threat of sharks to visitors of the world of coral. Wherever coral grows, sharks live. However, the dangers of shark attack are enormously greater, say, at Coney Island or the New Jersey shore, than they are in the Caribbean. In clear tropical waters, where both sharks and swimmers have a good view of the situation, attacks are uncommon. A snorkeler or Aqualunger can sight a shark a good way off, and is able to retreat to shallow, coral-cluttered water where the shark is not likely to follow. The shark, too, is less likely to start trouble if it can see clearly. In the cloudier waters of the Atlantic and Pacific shores, shark and swimmer often come together in a state of complete surprise—with unhappy results. But in the West Indies, sea urchins are a great deal more troublesome than sharks.

The moray eel must be classed with the reef creatures who are dangerous to man, although here again there is not much cause for alarm. Morays are fierce-looking, sharp-toothed fish of snakelike appearance that live the lives of hermits in rocky caverns on the reef. They reach lengths of six feet, but the most anyone is likely to see of a moray is the wicked-looking snout poking out of the cave as the eel waits for some unwary fish to pass nearby. A man who places his hand within reach of a moray will get bitten, and the eel is not likely to let go without a fight. The result can be a severe wound, and even the loss of an arm, but the moray eel strikes out only to defend itself, never to launch an unprovoked attack.

The moray is involved in one of those strange animal partnerships so common on the reef. It allows a small crustacean, the banded shrimp, to crawl along its jaw. The shrimp feeds on parasites that bother the eel; the moray even allows it to enter the toothy mouth and emerge unharmed. It is a wonderfully satisfying arrangement for both. The moray gets an efficient toothpicking service, while the shrimp, always hovering near the eel's frightening jaws, has a huge and valiant protector.

The fish we have been discussing in this chapter are complicated animals. They stand higher in the scale of evolution than any of the reef creatures. Fish have brains and eyes, bones and blood vessels. They are far more advanced than snails, clams, lobsters, and crabs, and they are vastly more intricate than such primitive, simple creatures as sponges and coral polyps.

Fish, then, are the lords and masters of the reef. They are the fastest, smartest, strongest of the reef creatures. However, two other members of the reef population have to be considered here. They stand midway between the boneless lower orders of animal life and the highly developed fish.

They are the squid and the octopus, which belong to the animal group known as *cephalopods*. That means "head-footed," and refers to the way their many tentacles sprout from the upper part of their bodies. Cephalopods are classed with the mollusks by zoologists. That makes them related to the snails and clams, which appears odd at first glance. Snails and clams seem little more than blobs of living flesh, sluggish and dim-witted, while squids and octopuses are active, complex, and fairly intelligent creatures. How can a snail and a squid be considered close relatives?

Unlikely as it seems, the squid and the octopus really are nothing but highly-developed mollusks. They have many feet instead of one, but their bodies are soft and boneless, and they eat by scraping their food with the rasping, tonguelike organ, the radula, just as snails do. Though most of the lower mollusks are protected by shells, cephalopods have only the bare remnant of a shell, carried within the body as an internal plate.

The octopus, whose name means "eight-footed," is common on the reef, but hard to spot. William Beebe, the naturalist and explorer, tells of coming upon an undersea boulder that had the shape of a row of giant steps. As he watched, "a bit of greenish black coral . . . began to move and crawl slowly downward, and with it went dangling things which I had taken for strands of dead seaweed. . . . The octopus climbed down, hesitated, felt about in different directions, and then descended the steps, flowing along the angles like some horrid viscid fluid in animal form."

During the day, the octopuses of the reef tuck themselves away in holes or crevices of the coral. Only rarely are they seen, glimpsed sometimes as a tangle of brownish tentacles stirring in some dark nook. At night, when the appearance of the reef is greatly transformed, the octopus prowls. Its eight twining, coiling tentacles are equipped with strong suckers that grab crabs or small fish and convey them toward the horny, parrotlike beak. A flabby, bag-shaped body comprises the remainder of the octopus. It has two useful defensive tactics: when irritated, it squirts a cloud of brown "ink," creating a smokescreen in the water that often allows it to escape. Also, it has the power to change its color to match its background. Pigmented cells just below the skin can be rapidly expanded or contracted, causing brown or violet patches to appear on the normally pink or white body of the octopus.

The octopus is shy, but not so its fellow cephalopod, the squid. A common sight is an armada of foot-long squids, cruising the reef in search of food. The creatures move with military precision, keeping a tight formation and rarely breaking ranks. Like an octopus, a squid has eight tentacles sprouting from its head, but there are also two longer arms that can shoot out to capture prey. The body has a cylindrical shape, with a fleshy mantle rimming it and serving in place of fins. The squids most often seen on coral reefs keep their many tentacles pressed tightly together in a way that resembles a beak, which leads observers to think they are seeing fish, not cephalopod mollusks.

There is something eerily graceful about the movements of a squid. It swims backward or forward with equal ease, gliding effortlessly and almost motionlessly through the water. Most of the time, the squid travels with its body end forward and its pressed-together tentacles behind it, but when it encounters danger it reverses itself smoothly and proceeds in the opposite direction without having to turn. It shares with the octopus the power to change its color and to spout an inky cloud of fluid, and when bothered by inquisitive human beings will usually go through a vivid cycle of hues, accompanied by angry spurts of dark ink.

When really faced with difficulties, the squid makes a jet-propelled escape. It sucks water into a cavity in its mantle and contracts its muscles, forcing a jet of water through a nozzle in back. This sends the squid shooting away at high speed, and the nozzle can be turned in any direction. Some authorities think that in short bursts squids are the fastest of all water-dwelling animals. Sometimes they move so swiftly that they catapult themselves from the water. Thor Heyerdahl, the Norwegian explorer who led the expedition of the raft *Kon-Tiki* across the Pacific, saw squids "flying" as high as six feet above the water. He wrote: "They pump seawater through themselves till they get up a terrific speed, and then they steer up at an angle from the surface by unfolding the pieces of skin like wings. Like the flying fish they make a glider flight over the waves for as far as their speed can carry them. . . . We often saw them sailing along for fifty or sixty yards, singly and in twos and threes."

Squids come in all sizes. The giant squids of the eastern Pacific weigh up to 350 pounds, and have bodies ten to twelve feet long, with tentacles more than fifty feet in length. Their powerful beaks can slash through thick wire. But the squids usually seen swimming in close ranks on the reef are no more than a foot or two long, and are often much smaller. In the narrow canyons of the coral reef there is no room for monsters.

5.

Scientists and Coral

Men have known about coral for thousands of years. The word itself was coined by the ancient Greeks, and one story has it that their term *korallion* meant "that which becomes hard when exposed to air." The Greeks thought that coral was flexible and soft in the sea, turning to stone only when plucked from the water.

That idea was wrong—but so was almost everything else that was believed about coral in ancient times. For centuries, men thought that the stony corals were minerals and the soft corals were plants. About 1700, the Italian chemist Ferrante Imperato argued that corals belonged to the animal kingdom, but other scientists of his time grouped the hard corals, the alcyonarian or soft ones, and the coralline algae in a special category that they called *zoophytes* ("animal-plants"), neither of one kingdom nor of the other.

Through most of the eighteenth century the argument raged as to whether corals were plants or animals. It is easy to sympathize with the bewilderment of the scientists. Most of the world's coral was in the tropics; most of the scientists lived in Europe. Studying living coral was a difficult matter two centuries ago. And the basic differences between plants and animals were very poorly understood.

We are aware today that plants are living things that make their own food. With the help of a green substance, chlorophyll, they use the sun's energy to combine carbon dioxide and water into food. This is the process known as photosynthesis. Animals, unable to manufacture their food, must gather it, feeding either on plants or on other animals. Another commonly drawn distinction between plants and animals is that most plants are rooted to one spot, while most animals are free to move about.

There are exceptions to all these statements. Some plants have no chlorophyll and get their food by stealing from other plants. Some are able to capture and digest animal life—the fly-catching pitcher plants and Venus flytrap, for instance. Some plants drift on the water, moving freely from place to place.

The scientists of the eighteenth century were willing to accept drifting algae as plants, but they had trouble with the idea that some animals might be rooted permanently in one place. Confronted with such stationary animals as corals and sponges, they grouped them with the plants.

A close study of coral showed that this was a mistake. The coral polyps might be stationary, but otherwise they behaved exactly as did other animals. They caught food with stinging tentacles and digested it. They responded to touch, heat, and light. They produced eggs that hatched into free-swimming young. In 1724, a Frenchman named Peyssonel investigated the Mediterranean corals and wrote that they were purely animal in nature. But the leading French authorities were so shocked by this declaration that they refused to let Peyssonel publish his findings in any scientific journal.

Without knowing of Peyssonel's work, the English naturalist John Ellis came to the same conclusions in 1755. He wrote:

"I own I am led to suspect that by much the greatest part of those Substances, which from their Figure have hitherto been reputed Sea Shrubs, Plants, Mosses, etc., are not only the Residence of Animals, but their Fabric likewise; and serve for the Purposes of Subsistence, Defense, and Propagation, as much as the Combs and Cells fabricated by Bees, and other Insects, serve for similar Purposes."

The next important scientist to express an opinion was Carl von Linné of Sweden, better known by his Latin name of Linnaeus. In the middle of the eighteenth century, Linnaeus set about the monumental task of classifying all living creatures according to a logical scheme of relationship. Much of his work was brilliant, but when he came to the corals he was hopelessly confused. He placed the madrepores and other stony corals correctly in the animal kingdom, but he classed many of the gorgonians with the ferns and mosses. He added a bewildering sentence referring to some of the soft corals that declared, "the stems are vegetable, but become animal when the creature flowers."

By this time European explorers had devoted considerable attention to the tropical coral reefs of the world. The great English navigator James Cook, making his second voyage of scientific research around the world, carried with him two German scientists, Johann Forster and his son Georg, who in 1775 examined the Pacific coral reefs. The Forsters provided the first really accurate account of coral polyps. By the start of the nineteenth century, the corals were clearly recognized as animals, and the last element of confusion disappeared when the hard algae were correctly shown to be plants.

Now the scientists at last understood the nature of the creatures that had built the coral reefs. But an enormously more difficult problem presented itself. How had the reefs themselves come into being?

Exploration had shown that there are three main types of coral reefs: fringing reefs, barrier reefs, and atolls. Fringing reefs, which are the type most common in the West Indies, begin close to the shoreline and extend perhaps a quarter of a mile into the sea. They create a broad stony platform, with active growth at the deep-water edge, and a slightly lower reef flat reaching back to the shore and covered with coral sand and other debris.

Barrier reefs are similar in structure to fringing reefs, but they are separated from the shore by channels that may be hundreds of feet deep and many miles wide. They may run parallel to a coast for great distances. Some barrier reefs in the Caribbean run a hundred miles or more, but these are dwarfed by the Great Barrier Reef of Australia, a wall of coral some 1,200 miles long, which in places is more than ninety miles from shore.

Atolls are not found near land at all. They are circular or horseshoe-shaped reefs arising in the open sea and enclosing shallow lagoons. Some atolls are forty or fifty miles across, perching atop submerged foundations that rise thousands of feet above the ocean floor. At some points the atoll reef may reach above the surface of the water, to form an island habitable by man. A great area of the Pacific is dotted with isolated atolls that have become inhabited islands.

These atolls fascinated the first European explorers who entered tropical waters. Probably the earliest account of an atoll is that of a sixteenth-century French voyager, François Pyrard de Laval, who was shipwrecked in the Indian Ocean on one of the atolls in the group known as the Maldive Islands. He wrote:

"Every Atollon is separated from others, and contains in itself a great multitude of small Isles; It is admirable to behold, how

that each of these Atollons are environed round with a huge
ledge of Rocks. . . . Being in the midst of an Atollon, you shall
see about you a great ledge of Rocks which impale and defend
the Isles, against the impetuousness of the Sea. But it is a very
fearful thing even to the most courageous to approach to this
ledge, and see the waves come afar off and break furiously on
every side. For I assure you, as a thing which I have seen a
thousand times, that the surge or billow is greater than a House,
and as white as Cotton: so that you shall view round about
you as it were a very white Wall, especially when the Sea is
lofty."

The navigators of the eighteenth century came to regard the
atolls as places of wonder and beauty. After sailing for weeks
across the deep, stormy Pacific, they would arrive at these jewel-
like rings of coral rimmed with graceful palm trees, and take
shelter on the placid green water of the lagoons. The atolls
seemed even more magical when it was learned that they were
built on foundations of coral. How had the tiny polyps reared
such huge islands in the middle of the trackless ocean?

That was a puzzle, indeed. It was easy enough to see how a
fringing reef could arise along the shores of an island or continent. Barrier reefs, many miles from land, were harder to explain. Most mysterious of all was the origin of the atolls,
hundreds or even thousands of miles from the nearest land.
By the start of the nineteenth century, it was understood that
reef-building corals could grow only in 150 feet or less of water.
It was impossible, then, that an atoll could have had its beginning
on the floor of the Pacific, thousands of feet down, growing upward over the centuries until it reached the surface.

Many theories were suggested to account for atoll formation.
The circular shape of most atolls reminded some observers of
the craters of volcanoes. What if drowned volcanoes existed

in the ocean, the rims of their craters fifty or a hundred feet below the surface? Young coral polyps would attach themselves to these rims, the theory held, and gradually form a ring-shaped reef with a lagoon in the center.

That sounded good. But thousands of atolls dot the Pacific and Indian Oceans, and it was fantastic to argue that there could be that many submerged volcanoes. Also, many atolls were more than fifty miles across, larger than the craters of any known volcanoes. Lastly, the reef-on-the-volcano-rim theory did not serve to explain the existence of barrier reefs, which presented a further puzzle.

The first real progress toward understanding the nature of coral reefs was the work of Charles Darwin. Darwin is famous for his theory of evolution, which he made public in 1859, stirring a storm of controversy with his ideas about the way living things had developed. Twenty years before that, Darwin had established his scientific reputation with a bold and superbly reasoned theory of coral reefs. All modern thinking about the structure of coral reefs is based on Darwin's ideas.

In 1831, when Charles Darwin was 22 and newly out of college, he took a post as naturalist aboard H.M.S. *Beagle*. The *Beagle* was about to leave on a five-year round-the-world cruise of scientific research, sponsored by the British government. As the vessel made its way across the Atlantic to Brazil, down the South American coast to Patagonia, around Cape Horn, and into the Pacific, young Darwin tirelessly studied the natural history of all he saw.

Late in 1835, after a long stay at the Galapagos Islands off the coast of Chile, the *Beagle* sailed westward across the Pacific. Some weeks later, Darwin noted in his journal that he saw "several of those most curious rings of coral land, just rising above the water's edge, which have been called Lagoon Islands."

He was awed by his first glimpse of atolls. "A long and bril-

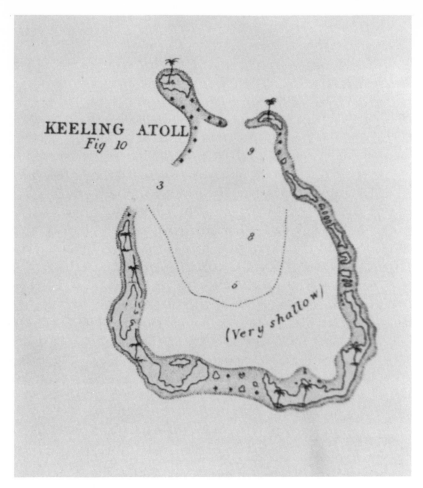

The atoll that inspired Darwin's reef theory, as shown in
Darwin's book on coral

liantly-white beach," he wrote, "is capped by a margin of green
vegetation: and the strip, looking either way, rapidly narrows
away in the distance, and sinks beneath the horizon. From the
mast-head, a wide expanse of smooth water can be seen within
the ring. These low hollow coral islands bear no proportion to

the vast ocean out of which they abruptly rise; and it seems wonderful that such weak invaders are not overwhelmed by the all-powerful and never-tiring waves of that great sea, miscalled the Pacific."

Darwin had already formed some ideas about coral reefs. Now, on the atoll known as Cocos-Keeling Island, he was able to make direct observations. His findings supported his original ideas. In 1837, when he was back in London, Darwin published a short article setting forth his beliefs. Two years later, he wrote a longer essay that was included in one of the many volumes of the scientific reports of the *Beagle* expedition. It attracted so much attention that in 1842 it appeared as a separate book, Darwin's first major scientific publication, under the title, *The Structure and Distribution of Coral Reefs*. The book went through many editions and in fact is still in print today.

Darwin declared that all barrier reefs and atolls began as simple fringing reefs. The reef corals and hard algae, he said, established themselves in tropical seas close to shore, where growing conditions were favorable. He then suggested that a *gradual sinking of the shoreline* took place while the reef was growing.

Both the land of the shore and the floor of the sea sank, Darwin said. If the sinking happened quickly, the coral reef would be carried below the 150-foot level and would drown. But if the submergence took place slowly, the reef would keep pace with it, the coral growing upward in the ever-deepening water. Although the coral at the bottom of the reef would eventually be carried below the growth level and die, there would always be living coral close to the surface, rising on a foundation of dead coral stone.

Darwin observed that coral grows more rapidly along the outer edge of a reef than at the shoreward side. He explained this by saying that at the shore, silt churned by the surf kills the coral; the ebbing of the tide, exposing shallow-water coral to the air, also has its fatal effect; and in extremely calm water, sheltered by thick coral growths, the polyps can be killed by stagnation. For all these reasons, Darwin said, a lagoon would tend to develop between the growing edge of the reef and the shore.

As the shoreline land kept sinking, the lagoon would grow wider. In time, the reef would be separated from the land by miles of open water. It would then be a barrier reef.

His explanation of atoll formation depended on the same idea of a sinking crust of the earth. Suppose, he said, a fringing reef developed around a high, rocky island. Gradual sinking began; as the island settled into the water, the reef continued to grow, always maintaining itself just a few feet below the surface. A time would come when a broad lagoon rimmed by coral reefs surrounded the disappearing island. This would have the form of a continuous barrier reef encircling the island. But at last even the top of the island would be covered by water. The reef, still keeping up with the general sinking movement of its foundation, now would be a ring of coral enclosing a lagoon—that is, an atoll.

That was the heart of Darwin's theory. It was simple and direct. Constant growth of coral reefs in shallow water, combined with steady sinking of the land—that was how he accounted for the otherwise puzzling presence of atolls at surface level in an ocean several miles deep.

Soon after Darwin published his theory, an American geologist named James Dwight Dana gave support to its most controversial feature. Darwin explained everything in terms of sinking land—but where was the scientific evidence to prove that such sinking had taken place? Dana showed that many reef-fringed islands are cut by deep bays, inlets, and indentations. These, said Dana, were ancient river valleys that had been flooded by the sea when the land began to sink. Standing on the

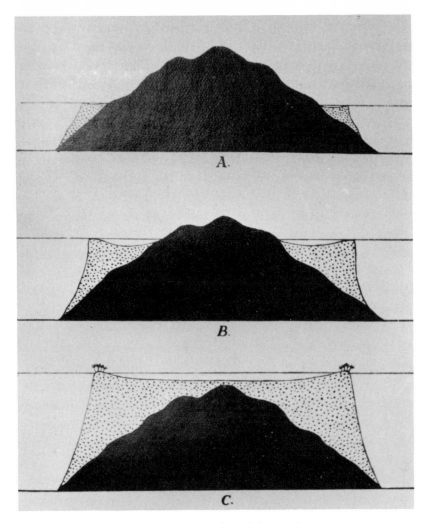

Darwin's theory of reef formation:

a) fringing reef surrounding a mountainous island;
b) island gradually sinking;
c) island below sea level; atoll formed.

summit of a mountain on Tahiti, Dana saw that, "Sunk to any level above that of five hundred feet, the erosion-made valleys of Tahiti would become deep bays, and above that of one thousand feet, fjord-like bays, with the ridges spreading in the water like spider's legs."

Dana's studies provided strong support for Darwin's theories. Many scientists immediately accepted the Darwin-Dana concept of sinking land. Others had strong objections. If this process of sinking had been going on for so long, why were the atoll lagoons never deeper than 100 or 150 feet? And how did Mr. Darwin explain the fact that many of the Indian Ocean atolls stand nine or ten feet above the surface of the water? That would indicate that the land is *rising*, not sinking! Also, in some places all three kinds of reef, fringing, barrier, and atoll, could be found together. According to Darwin's theory, that was impossible.

Darwin soon became enmeshed in his work on evolution, and left it to other men to defend his coral-reef ideas. They answered the critics in various ways. The lagoons, they said, were shallow because of silting and filling. The dry land of the Indian Ocean atolls, they claimed, had resulted from the hurling of coral boulders ashore in storms, or perhaps from a purely local and recent raising of the land level. As for reefs of mixed types, they developed through tilting of the land, perhaps—one end of an island sinking and the other end rising.

Darwin's critics spoke louder and louder. Several new theories of atoll formation were put forth.

One of them was the work of John Murray, a naturalist who traveled around the world between 1872 and 1876 aboard the scientific research vessel H.M.S. *Challenger*. Murray could not accept Darwin's notion of sinking land. He proposed a totally opposite idea. Volcanic action, he said, elevated the sea floor in places. Submerged mountains were thrust upward to become platforms for coral growth. If these newly created mountains reached above the water surface, erosion would eventually cut them down until they were a hundred feet or so below the surface; then reefs could begin to form. If the peaks of the drowned mountains were too deep for reef growth, a steady rain of shells, bones, algae, and silt would ultimately build them high enough to allow the formation of coral reefs. Once the corals were established, Murray said, they would grow toward the surface. The outer rim of the reef, nourished by the fresh water, would grow faster, reaching the surface first to give the reef a cuplike shape. The corals in the center, choked by silt and cut off from the open sea, would grow more slowly, and eventually would die. The action of sea water would dissolve the dead coral in the center, forming and deepening the lagoon. The end result would be a ring-shaped atoll enclosing a body of shallow water—formed, according to Murray, without the need of inventing a theory of land-sinking at all.

The scientific world was split. Was the land sinking or rising? Was Darwin right, or Murray?

One way to settle the dispute was to drill a hole through the rim of an atoll and see what its foundation was made of. If Darwin were correct, coral rock would be found at depths of many hundreds of feet, deposited long ago when the sea floor was much higher than it is now. But if Murray's theory were true, the atoll would be no more than about 150 feet thick, with some other kind of rock underlying it.

The atoll of Funafuti in the Ellice Islands, north of Fiji, was chosen as the site for the experiment. Darwin himself had suggested the project. "I wish," he had written, "that some doubly rich millionaire would take it into his head to have borings made in some of the Pacific and Indian atolls, and bring back cores for slicing from a depth of 500 or 600 feet."

Darwin made that suggestion in 1881, the year before his death. When the experiment was carried out, in 1897, it seemed to prove Darwin's theory. A hole 1,114 feet deep was drilled, and showed coral all the way down. At the very bottom were signs of the presence of a typical shallow-water coral, which could never have grown at such depths. The drilling appeared to show that the atoll had risen, layer by layer, while the under-lying crust of the earth had subsided more than a thousand feet.

Murray's supporters would not admit defeat. They argued that in any coral reef fragments of coral were constantly being broken off by storms. These coral chunks landed in the sea just beyond the living reef, and could very well build up a towering heap of stone. The Funafuti boring, they insisted, had quite pos-sibly drilled through nothing more significant than a thousand-foot-thick rubble pile in the sea.

So the matter remained unsettled. In 1910, Professor Reginald A. Daly of Harvard University complicated it by adding a new theory, that of glacial control. Seven decades had passed since Darwin had done his work on coral reefs, and scientists had dis-covered evidence of several ice ages during the past million years. For long periods of time, it now was known, the overall temperature of the earth had dropped several degrees, and much of the planet's land surface had been covered by sheets of ice. Daly suggested that during these ice ages, so much water was piled up on land in the form of ice that the level of the seas was lowered by several hundred feet. This would have left all existing coral reefs high and dry, and would, of course, have killed them. Therefore all of today's coral reefs, according to Daly, are young ones, formed in the hundred centuries or so since the end of the last ice age.

The dead coral reefs provided platforms in the sea. Somehow coral polyps survived in parts of the world, and when normal weather conditions returned and the ice began to melt, these polyps built new reefs on the platforms left by the dead reefs. As the world warmed, the sea level rose and the new reefs rose with it. This, said Daly, would account for barrier reefs and even for atolls, without the need of bringing in the Darwin-Dana notion of sinking land.

Daly's ideas had a great deal of merit. Darwin had not taken into account at all the raising and lowering of the sea level in successive ice ages, and obviously that was a factor to be reckoned with in any theory of reef growth. Much that was puzzling about the small reefs of the West Indies became clearer when considered in terms of Daly's views. For instance, there are no true atolls in the West Indies. Did that mean that Darwin's land-subsidence had not taken place there? The new theory provided an answer. The West Indian reefs were only ten or twenty thousand years old, resting on older ones killed by exposure during the last ice age. They were so young that subsidence, an extremely slow process at best, had not had a chance to play any part in their formation.

The Daly theory of glacial control could not replace the Darwin and Murray explanations of atoll formation. A change of a few hundred feet in sea level was not enough to account for the existence of atolls in water many miles deep. For more than thirty years after Daly entered the field, scientists debated what had become known as the "coral-reef problem." New research kept changing the picture. Now Darwin was in favor, and now Murray. Daly had his supporters, too.

The advance of geology in the twentieth century showed that the earth's crust is far from being the solid, inflexible thing that most nineteenth-century geologists imagined. Rather, it is in constant though gradual change—some parts rising, other parts sinking. New mountains are being forced upward; old ones are subsiding. These discoveries gave heart both to the Darwin and the Murray forces, since each group based its ideas on such shifts in land levels.

More drilling seemed in order, because the 1897 experiment

at Funafuti had failed to give conclusive results. In 1926, a hole more than 600 feet deep on the Great Barrier Reef showed evidence of coral all the way down. Cores taken off Florida and on various Pacific atolls also indicated coral at great depths. None of these cores succeeded in reaching the floor of hard, non-coralline rock that Darwin said lay beneath all atolls.

After the Second World War, new and deeper drillings were made. On Bikini Atoll in the Pacific, a hole went down 2,556 feet in 1947. It bottomed in coral, as did a 1,285-foot drilling on Eniwetok Atoll in 1951. In the summer of 1952, a determined effort was made to get to the bottom of an atoll's foundation at last. A group of American geologists led by Harry Ladd went to work at Elugelab Islet on Eniwetok Atoll, in the Marshall Islands. Their goal was the layer of basalt, a hard rock of volcanic origin, that was thought to be underneath all the coral.

Time was against them. In November, 1952, Eniwetok was scheduled to be the site of the world's first hydrogen bomb explosion. The geologists painted the slogan, "Basalt or Bust," on their shack, and got to work. Down went the drill. Fossil coral came up. Two thousand, three thousand, four thousand feet down, and still coral was found. At 4,630 feet, progress became slow, indicating that hard rock had been reached. Before a sample could be brought up, though, the hole collapsed and the geologists had to start all over. Racing to finish their work before the H-bomb test forced them to leave the atoll, they drilled a new hole 4,222 feet deep, and this time brought up basalt. Darwin's daring idea had been confirmed. The atoll consisted of thousands of feet of dead coral, resting on a floor of volcanic rock that once had been less than two hundred feet below sea level. The geologists calculated that Eniwetok Atoll has been sinking at an average rate of four one-hundredths of an inch per century for the past sixty million years.

Postwar research provided a second proof of Darwin's theory.

In 1946, an American deep-sea geologist named Harry Hess took soundings of the Pacific floor and discovered the existence of hundreds of flat-topped peaks rising from the bottom to a level about a mile below sea level. Dredges brought up rock samples that showed that these seamounts are made up of basalt and other volcanic minerals, and are covered with the fossil remains of shallow-water corals. In short, these are drowned islands that once reached to the surface of the ocean and now lie under a mile of water—backing Darwin's belief that the earth's crust has been sinking over a wide area.

The seamounts also gave support to John Murray's theory that atolls can form on pedestals thrust upward through the ocean by volcanic action. Before the undersea islands found by Harry Hess had subsided, they first had had to arise. At some time in the past, then, the boiling, turbulent zone of fire beneath the earth's crust had pushed mountains upward through the sea and coral reefs had formed at their crests. Later, a general process of sinking began, drowning the mountains and forming the barrier reefs and atolls as outlined by Darwin.

As usually happens when a number of contradictory scientific theories are offered, it turns out that no one theory has a monopoly on truth. We know today that Darwin was right about the sinking of the land, but that does not mean that *all* reefs were formed that way. John Murray correctly suggested that many reefs grew at the summits of underwater mountains that had been forced upward by volcanic action. And Reginald Daly's glacial control theory shed light on the development of fringing reefs in seas whose levels were raised and lowered during the ice ages.

So coral reefs are formed in a number of ways, some on sinking coasts, some on volcanically uplifted pedestals, some on platforms of dead coral left behind by the ice ages. Darwin was right, though, to argue that most atolls and barrier reefs were produced by the sinking of the ocean floor. Corals could not have grown upward from great depths; they must have lived near the surface, in the shallow, well-lit waters that they require, building their stony skeletons steadily and untiringly while the foundation below them slowly sank. Putting forth this theory when he did, at a time when practically nothing was known of the earth's structure, was one of the most remarkable feats of Charles Darwin's astonishing scientific career.

6.

The Geography of Coral

W hen Darwin published his book on coral in 1842, he included a map that showed the location of all known reefs.
Different colors showed the different types of reef: red for
fringing reefs, pale blue for barrier reefs, and bright blue for
atolls.

A great deal has been learned about geography since Darwin
drew his map, but it is still surprisingly up-to-date. The huge
land mass he labelled New Holland is now called Australia;
Hindoostan has become India and Pakistan; what he called
Cochinchina is familiar to us as Laos, Vietnam, and Cambodia.
The political changes have been great, but little needs to be added
to Darwin's coral-reef geography.

Darwin's map shows a vast barrier reef off the eastern coast
of Australia, and smaller ones in the Pacific and the Red Sea.
It shows hundreds of atolls strung out across thousands of miles
of the Pacific, and other chains of them in the Indian Ocean. It
indicates fringing reefs down the eastern coast of Africa as far
as Mozambique and Madagascar, around many of the islands of
the West Indies, and surrounding the Pacific island group he

calls the Sandwich Islands, today the State of Hawaii. That
is all. Darwin indicates no reefs along the western coasts of
Africa, the Americas, or Australia, and none that lie very far
north of the Tropic of Cancer or south of the Tropic of Capricorn.

For some reason Darwin did not include the eastern coast of
Brazil on his map, although he knew there were fringing reefs
there. That is the only significant omission from his chart. Otherwise he included all important coral locations. Today's maps
of coral distribution classify the Red Sea formations as fringing
reefs, not barrier reefs, and include Bermuda as an atoll, the
only one in the Atlantic, but basically they follow Darwin's plan.

Why are coral reefs found only in these places—the Pacific
and Indian Oceans, the Caribbean Sea, and along the eastern
coasts of Africa, Australia, and South America?

We have already seen that corals of the reef-building type
have very special requirements for growth. They need water
temperature above 70° F., and perish in places where the winter
temperature drops below 65°. That immediately eliminates all
but the tropical and subtropical seas. They must have shallow
water, less than 150 feet deep. That eliminates most of the
ocean, except where special underwater conditions produce platforms for their growth. Fresh water kills them, so coral reefs
will not grow where rivers reach the sea, or where the rainfall
is unusually high. On the other hand, they cannot grow where
the water is too salty; as much as a 4.8% level of salt in the sea
is fatal. They must have fairly clear water, low in smothering
silts and sediments.

Where all these requirements are met, we have coral reefs.

Geographers divide the tropics into four "life zones." They
are the Atlantic Tropical American, the Pacific Tropical American, the Indo-West Pacific, and the West African zones. Coral

reefs are found in the Atlantic Tropical and Indo-West Pacific zones, but not in the West African or Pacific Tropical ones.

The richest coral growths are in the Indo-West Pacific zone, which ranges from the Hawaiian Islands to the eastern coast of Africa. In this large zone, which includes the Indian Ocean and more than half of the Pacific, are found most of the atolls, as well as the Great Barrier Reef, the biggest single coral formation in the world.

East of this zone, stretching from the mid-Pacific to the western shores of the Americas, is a region of ocean that is too cool for coral reefs to thrive in. Since there are few islands in this zone, the Pacific Tropical, the development of fringing reefs would be difficult even if the water were warm enough. So no reefs exist off the western shores of Mexico, Central America, and South America.

The Atlantic Tropical American zone, taking in the Caribbean, the Gulf of Mexico, and the eastern coast of South America, has coral reefs that are generally of the fringing kind, and a few small barrier reefs. The island of Bermuda, which lies well outside the tropics, is included in this zone, and has the world's northernmost living coral reefs.

To the east of the Atlantic Tropical zone lies another area of cold ocean water, reaching as far as the western coast of Africa. This keeps reefs out of the West African life zone, despite the tropical appearance of the African coast.

The presence or absence of reefs in these zones of life in the tropics depends entirely on ocean currents. It happens that the western shores of all the continents are bathed by cold currents, preventing reef formation.

Currents can be thought of as rivers in the ocean. Some are warm, some are cold; they flow in paths that can be mapped and studied, and have had a great effect on the world's history, both

by affecting the climates of certain countries and by providing
helps or hindrances to navigation.

Many factors are involved in the forming of ocean currents,
all interconnected so that it is hard to say where the true beginning lies. The winds are responsible for shaping the currents,
but the currents influence the winds as well. Wherever the
process starts, we can at least say that the currents are pushed
along by the force of the wind. Blowing steadily across the face
of the sea, the winds form ripples and waves, and drive the water
forward. In the tropics, the most reliable winds are the trade
winds, which blow from the northeast above the Equator and
from the southeast below it. They set in motion a great stream
of westward-moving water, whose course is altered by the spin
of the earth on its axis.

One current formed in this way is the North Equatorial Current, which comes westward across the Atlantic toward the
Americas. As it passes through the islands of the West Indies,
this current splits, part turning northward toward the United
States and part continuing into the Gulf of Mexico. Water piles
up in the Gulf and is forced northward around Florida, where
the two parts of the North Equatorial Current rejoin as the Gulf
Stream. This swift, narrow current bears warm water from the
tropics up the eastern coast of North America until it hits the cold
Labrador Current coming from the north. This forces the Gulf
Stream across the Atlantic, delivering its warmth to Great Britain
and the other countries of northern Europe. Thanks to the Gulf
Stream, countries like Norway and Sweden have relatively mild
climates though they lie as far to the north as frigid Labrador.

The Gulf Stream next turns southward toward Africa. By now
it has given up its warmth, and carries cold water from Europe
past the Azores and the northwest coast of Africa. Finally it is
picked up by the trade winds, which drive it back across the

Atlantic again as the North Equatorial Current, gaining new warmth as it passes through the tropics.

The Atlantic currents, then, are something like a great wheel, moving westward along the vicinity of the Tropic of Cancer, carrying warm water through the West Indies and along the United States, shunting eastward again in the North Atlantic to bring warmth to Europe, and completing the circle by brushing Africa with cold water. It was this current that carried Columbus westward; if he had sailed a more northerly course, he might never have reached the Americas. The skippers of sailing vessels quickly learned to ride the North Equatorial Current from Europe to the Americas, and the Gulf Stream when going the other way.

This wheel of water carries enough warmth northward to permit coral reefs to develop at Bermuda. On the other side of the Atlantic, it brings enough cold water southward to prevent the growth of coral along the coast of Morocco, Guinea, and the other countries of northwest Africa. Meanwhile the South Equatorial Current is also at work below the Equator, and one of its branches, the Benguela Current, chills the ocean off Angola and its neighbors of southwest Africa.

The South Equatorial Current is the coral-killing villain in the Pacific, too. It travels a great counterclockwise swing, cooling the coasts of Chile and Peru. That section of the current is known as the Humboldt Current, named for the great German scientist of the early nineteenth century, Alexander von Humboldt. For many years, oceanographers believed that the Humboldt Current carried cold water up from the Antarctic. Now it is thought that a much more complex process is at work. Strong winds off the South American coast apparently blow the surface water of the Humboldt Current out to sea, causing cold water from the depths to well upward. Whatever the reason, the eastern Pacific is too cold for coral reefs, as is the water of the Indian Ocean off Australia's western coast.

Where the currents permit, the reefs develop—lushly, in the Indo-West Pacific zone, and sparingly, in the Atlantic Tropical zone. Reginald Daly's glacial control theory gives us a reason why the West Indian reefs are so small. The effects of the ice age changes in sea level were much greater in the Caribbean than in the deep-water basins of the Pacific and Indian Oceans. Daly showed that where coral existed close to the continents— as in the West Indies—the reefs were exposed to the air and destroyed by the drop in sea level, and the coral organisms were unable to re-establish themselves at the lower levels because of the colder temperatures that then prevailed. Only when the earth grew warm again could the reefs return, and the ones we see today are no more than 10,000 to 25,000 years old—newcomers, in the geological scheme of things.

The West Indian reefs are still impressive sights, except to someone who has seen the majestic reefs of the Pacific. Nearly every Caribbean island has a fringing reef, and a few have off-shore barrier reefs. The typical West Indian reef can be reached by swimmers setting out from shore, but many of the most sizable reefs are half a mile or more out and must be visited by boat. The fairly big reefs of Jamaica are in this class. At Antigua, though, a quite extensive reef can be seen fewer than fifty yards offshore, a safe and easy swim.

Cuba has a well-developed barrier reef that runs westward for more than a hundred miles from Havana on the north coast, and at one point stands twenty miles offshore. The barrier reef of Cuba's southern coast, the finest in the West Indies, runs for 150 miles, and in places is separated from shore by a lagoon thirty-five miles wide and sixty to seventy feet deep. Another fine barrier reef is found for some 100 miles along the eastern shore of Andros Island, in the Bahamas. It grows near the edge of a submerged cliff facing the trade winds. Not far to windward beyond the reef, the sea drops to depths of more than a mile.

A smaller reef, but one of the most beautiful in the Caribbean, lies in the channel that separates St. Croix, American Virgin Islands, from uninhabited Buck Island. The water here is unusually clear, and the large stands of elkhorn and staghorn coral give the reef an appearance of rich complexity. Since St. Croix is an American possession, the U.S. National Park Service has taken charge of the Buck Island reef, setting up an underwater snorkeling trail with labels to indicate the most important sights. Buck Island can be reached by a short boat trip from the

The author snorkeling at St. John, Virgin Islands

northeast shore of St. Croix. The National Park Service also maintains a labeled underwater snorkeling trail at Trunk Bay on the island of St. John, American Virgin Islands. This is not on a deep-water reef, however, but on a small though highly attractive fringing reef surrounding a little island in the bay close to shore.

There are two places actually within the United States where coral reefs can be seen. The Hawaiian Islands are fringed by coral, and the reefs are extremely interesting, though small. One outstanding location is Coconut Island, in Kaneohe Bay, off the island of Oahu. Here, only half an hour by boat from Honolulu, the capital of the fiftieth state, the University of Hawaii maintains a marine research laboratory. More than 2,500 species of marine life have been found in the warm, shallow waters of Kaneohe Bay.

Closer to home for most Americans are the reefs of Florida. The Florida Keys, that chain of islands reaching southwestward for nearly two hundred miles off Florida's eastern coast, were in part formed by coral polyps; the eastern islands, from Sands to Loggerhead Key, are the 110-mile-long remnants of a dead reef that thrived before the last ice age. On the seaward side of this island chain lies a wall of living coral, separated from the Keys by a lagoon three to seven miles wide and less than thirty feet deep.

For many years this great reef was under severe attack by the most dangerous animal in the world—man. Curio dealers from Miami Beach were raiding it, using dynamite and crowbars to pull up huge chunks of coral to be sold to tourists. Sponges and conchs, ripped from the sea by thousands, were stacked high on roadside stands throughout Florida. Spearfishermen swam over the reef, stabbing at everything that moved, including one another.

Florida conservationists, realizing that the reef would be

ruined if this sort of treatment went on, took action. The Florida Board of Parks and Historic Memorials set aside a seventy-five-square-mile section, ten per cent of the entire reef, as a permanent nature preserve. Since part of the reef lies in waters under federal jurisdiction, the United States Government matched Florida's action. Today the protected area is known by two names, indicating the joint state and federal decision. President Eisenhower proclaimed the Key Largo Coral Reef Preserve in March 1960, and in dedication ceremonies the following December, Florida's Governor Leroy Collins gave it the additional name of John Pennekamp Coral Reef State Park, in honor of a local newspaperman and conservationist.

John Pennekamp Park, the world's first entirely underwater park, is twenty-five miles from Miami Beach and only three miles from Key Largo. Thousands of sightseers visit it each year. The more cautious ones look down on the splendor of the coral through the hulls of glass-bottomed boats, but many don mask and snorkel for a closer view, or wear underwater breathing units to descend into the coral world. Rod-and-reel fishing is still permitted, but spearfishing is not. Naturally, the destructive mining of the coral itself is prohibited. In their steady way, the coral polyps are rapidly repairing the damage inflicted by years of commercial greed.

The Red Sea, that narrow, 1,500-mile-long stretch of water separating Arabia and Africa, is another place where reef-building corals flourish. The northern reaches of the Red Sea have small, stunted reefs, but the central part of the sea, off the coasts of Saudi Arabia and the Sudan, offers a magnificent coral display. Jacques-Yves Cousteau, who has explored the Red Sea several times, tells of "bank after bank of exuberant coral structures, second only to those of the Great Barrier Reef in extent and exceeding it perhaps in splendor. Here there is deep clarity, blazing color, and active fauna living under the most arid and least populated of coasts."

The largest Red Sea reef, according to Captain Cousteau, is the nearly uncharted Far-San bank, "350 miles long and thirty miles wide, or six million acres of submerged reefs and isles along the Hedjaz and Yemen coasts." He calls it a "demented masterpiece of outcrops, shoals, foaming reefs, and other lurking ship-breakers."

The Red Sea flows into the Gulf of Aden, whose waters meet those of the Arabian Sea and the Indian Ocean. Little or no coral is found here; the next reefs are encountered well down the East African coast, fringing the shores of Somaliland, Kenya, and Zanzibar. The large island of Madagascar has extensive fringing reefs, but the coral goes no further south. The Indian Ocean has three important chains of coral atolls, the Laccadive, Maldive, and Chagos Islands. Hundreds of miles to the east, alone in the sea due south of Sumatra, is Cocos-Keeling Atoll, famous as the place where Darwin made his classic reef studies. The many islands of Indonesia have fringing coral reefs, as do the Philippines. As we continue eastward, we enter the Western Pacific—the true home of coral.

Many of the westernmost Pacific islands are volcanic in origin —the tops of submerged mountain chains. The Solomon Islands, New Hebrides, Carolines, and Marianas belong to this group. Nearly all have fringing reefs. New Caledonia, a large island that once was part of a continent now lost, is rimmed by a mighty barrier reef. The high, rocky Fiji Islands also have encircling barrier reefs, though not so big.

North of Fiji are coral atoll groups: the Marshall Islands, the Gilberts, the Ellices. To the east are the Tonga Islands, coral reefs that have been raised from the sea by volcanic action. Further eastward are the volcanic Society Islands, including famed Tahiti, and the sprawling Tuamotu Archipelago of coral

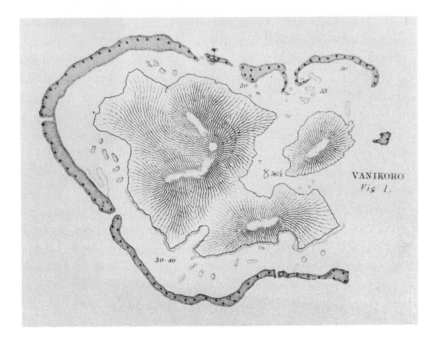

**A large Pacific atoll, as illustrated in Darwin's book
on coral reefs (1842)**

atolls. North of these are the Marquesa Islands, of volcanic
origin. They rise so steeply from the deep waters surrounding
them that not even a fringing reef can establish itself on their
shores. Finally, well to the east, we reach the Hawaiian Islands,
the last great Pacific group, with their small reefs. Beyond lies
cool water and no coral reefs.

In this eastward path through the Pacific, we have overlooked
one zone of coral: the Great Barrier Reef of Australia. It was
no error; that reef is so mighty it needs a chapter of its own,
and should not be compressed into a quick survey.

One notable point about the worldwide distribution of corals
is that the same types of coral are found everywhere, as well
as the same general kind of reef-dwelling creatures. Elkhorn and

staghorn coral are universal, as are brain coral, fire coral, spiny sea urchins, sting rays, starfish, gorgonians, and the rest. Of course, there are local variations in color, shape, and size. Certain forms, also, are confined to single areas. Mushroom coral is found only on the Pacific reefs, for example, and so are the poisonous cone shells and the horrid stonefish. The Great Barrier Reef, with its immense area, shelters hundreds of reef-dwelling species not known on the small reefs of the West Indies. But these local variations are not surprising. What is remarkable is the global spread of so many creatures.

Consider the problem involved. Elkhorn coral exists in the Caribbean, and on the Great Barrier Reef, half a world away. But how did the coral polyps get from one zone to the other? They certainly did not march overland across South and Central America. Nor could they have survived the swim through the chilly sub-Antarctic waters around Cape Horn. Given present conditions, it is hard to see how any tropical species could have spread from the Pacific to the Caribbean, or vice versa.

Geologists give us part of the answer. They have shown that the land bridge connecting North America and South America is relatively recent. Until a few million years ago, what is now Central America was mostly under water, allowing free passage between the Pacific and the Caribbean. The young polyps, drifting on the open seas, could have made journeys of thousands of miles before finding shelter and starting the building of reefs.

Even this explanation, which disposes of the land barrier between the two seas, still is incomplete. How did the delicate polyps survive that long swim through the cool waters of the eastern Pacific?

The record of the rocks tells us. Geologists, studying fossil evidence, have concluded that the world's climate has changed many times. Not only have there been ice ages, but there have been eras when much of the world had what we would consider a tropical climate. Coral reefs, now confined to a band around the middle of our planet, once were much more extensive.

Fossil corals have been found in many regions. The earliest ones, about 400 million years old, belong to an extinct group called the *Tetracoralla*, a name that refers to the fact that the stony partitions, or septa, grew in multiples of four. The modern stony corals, which appeared some 180 million years ago when dinosaurs existed, are termed *Hexacoralla*, since their septa grow in multiples of six. The alcyonarian or soft corals, with eight tentacles and eight partitions, are the *Octocoralla*, and they date from about 350 million years ago.

The evidence of fossils shows that coral reefs grew in many surprising places. About 300 million years ago, for example, a warm, shallow sea covered parts of Indiana, Illinois, and Wisconsin. Ancient coral reefs seventy-five feet thick and several miles long have been uncovered there. Since coral is a fairly soft rock with many pores, pools of oil sometimes have accumulated in ancient reefs. One good oil field in southern Illinois is located in a buried reef hundreds of millions of years old.

Perhaps 280 million years ago, the warm inland sea spread to include much of what is now the United States. Fine deposits of fossil coral have been found in such places as Kentucky, Iowa, Michigan, and western New York. About 50 million years later, a magnificent barrier reef existed in a still less likely part of the country—southern New Mexico and Texas. This great reef was thousands of feet thick and hundreds of miles long—the equal or even the superior of the Great Barrier Reef. Today part of it can be seen as a mountain range overlooking the parched desert, running from Carlsbad Caverns, New Mexico, to El Capitan Peak in Texas, forty-five miles away. Other small sections of the reef are exposed nearby, but for more than 350 miles of its course it is hidden by layers of rock deposited in more recent times.

It may be hard to think of New Mexico and Texas, with their

sagebrush-and-cactus dryness, providing a friendly environment for coral reefs. But it is more difficult yet to imagine cold, rainy England crisscrossed by reefs, as it was some 200 million years ago. Sweden has even older reefs, formed when Scandinavia was bathed by tropical seas. Snowy Russia, too, once lay in the coral-reef zone; the western slopes of the South Ural mountain range contain limestone deposits more than 150 feet thick, laid down by coral polyps about 210 million years ago.

These ancient seas retreated long before the first mammals evolved. Some seventy million years ago, the area of coral life was still broad enough to include Georgia and Alabama as well as the West Indies, but the fossil record shows a steady shrinkage of the coral zone. During the ice ages that gripped the earth again and again over the past million years, reefs in most of the world must have been wiped out, only those close to the equator surviving. There is reason to think that the retreat of coral is still taking place, even in today's fairly mild climate. The spread of mankind has brought pollution to the tropical seas; motor fuels and sewage deposits have injured reefs on some West Indian islands, and the growth of others is slowing down. Some day the polyps may be unable to restore the reefs as fast as their enemies —wind and storm, pollution, and coral-destroying animal life —tear them down. A time may come when the wonderful splendor of the coral reefs is only a fading memory of a bygone era of natural history.

7.

The Great Barrier Reef

Any list of the great natural wonders of the world must include some unavoidable choices. The Grand Canyon of the Colorado, that vast and many-hued gash in the earth's surface, is sure to be on the list. So is thundering Niagara Falls, and the mighty Amazon River, and cloud-piercing Mount Everest. And one that is surely impossible to omit is the Great Barrier Reef, fantastic and dazzling in its spectacular size and beauty.

The dry statistics of the Great Barrier Reef only hint at its immensity. It is some 1,260 miles long, and encloses an area of 80,000 square miles. If by some magic the reef could be transported to the United States, it would run from Massachusetts to Alabama, or from Los Angeles to Denver, or from Nebraska to Pennsylvania. The reef is many miles wide and several hundred feet deep.

It is not, though, a solid wall of coral. Rather, the Great Barrier Reef is an intricate maze of coral reefs, shoals, and islands, broken again and again by channels. It lies in the Pacific off Australia's eastern coast, and its outer edge varies in distance from that coast, ten miles away in some places, 150 miles away

in others. The average width of the channel between Australia
and the reef is twenty to thirty miles.

The coral grows most densely at the north end of the reef,
which is the part closest to the tropics—for Australia lies south
of the Equator, and the sea is cooler and less favorable for coral
growth as more southerly latitudes are reached. The Tropic of
Capricorn, which is virtually the southern boundary of the world
of coral, runs across the heart of Australia. The Great Barrier
Reef does not continue far below it. At its northern end, reaching
almost to the coast of New Guinea, the reef is awesomely thick
and nearly unbroken. As it moves into cooler waters, it becomes
less of a barrier, and lies at a greater distance from shore. The
barrier part of the reef proper ends at Swain Reefs, about midway down the Australian coast. For a few hundred miles after
that, only scattered reefs and coral islets are found, and from
a point called Sandy Cape southward the coast is clear of coral.
Such important Australian ports as Brisbane and Sydney lie
well to the south of the coral zone.

The Great Barrier Reef, then, is really a series of reefs, of
all sizes and shapes, forming a helter-skelter cluster along the
Australian coast. Professor Beete Jukes, the first naturalist to
make a careful study of the Barrier, described it this way in
a report published in 1846:

> If it were to be laid dry, this great Barrier would be
> found to have a considerable resemblance to a gigantic and
> irregular fortification . . . crowned with a broken parapet
> wall, and carried from one rising ground to another. The
> tower-like bastions, of projecting and detached reefs, would
> increase this resemblance.

At its southern end the Barrier lies almost 150 miles from
the coast. This creates a sheltered waterway sometimes called
Australia's "Grand Canal." Ships heading northward from

Brisbane can sail within the reef for many miles without en-
countering coral, since the channel is wide and deep. Gradually
the reef nears the coast, cutting the waterway to a width of fifty
miles, then to twenty, finally to ten. Coral islands become more
numerous. At low tide, acres of coral are exposed to view, several
feet above the water level. This regular exposure does not kill
the coral.

Above the midway point, the reef parts company with the
shore again, and at one point it is some eighty miles from the
coast. Here, in the region of greatest coral growth, the Barrier
becomes a confusing and irregular mass of reefs broken by small
channels. Passage by boat becomes almost impossible.

Most people who see the reef view it from its landward side
—that is, from the channel that separates it from the mainland.
This great waterway is shallow and calm, since the bulk of the
reef serves as a gigantic breakwater to the east. Submerged coral
reefs, visible at low tide, can be visited on short boat excursions.
Also found in this channel are numerous rocky islands, not
formed by coral growth at all. These are the tops of drowned
mountains—for, as Darwin guessed and later scientists have
proven, a widespread sinking of land has taken place in this
part of the world. The rocky islands of the channel once were
the cliffs of the Australian shore. The Barrier, lying so many
miles out to sea, was once a fringing reef right along that shore.
But the shore subsided, and the sea flooded the coast, turning
mountaintops into islands and producing a barrier reef where a
fringing reef had been.

Not very many travelers venture far into the tangled, dangerous byways of the Great Barrier Reef. They are content to explore its western side, the inner reefs. The coral zone, though,
is many miles wide, and a few brave souls have made the treach-
erous journey through the Barrier to its outer, or Pacific side.
The reef is quite different there. No longer is there a shallow

channel dotted with islands. On the eastern edge of the Barrier, looking outward, one has a baffling immensity of coral behind one, and all the mind-numbing hugeness of the Pacific Ocean ahead.

One of those who made the journey to the outer edge of the reef was C. M. Yonge, leader of the Great Barrier Reef Expedition of 1928-29, a major scientific undertaking. In his book, *A Year on the Great Barrier Reef*, Yonge described the awesome trip.

The scientists traveled in the *Luana*, a wooden boat sheathed with copper. One man stood by the mast as lookout, pointing to the coral reefs while the helmsman made his way through the narrow passages. They could travel only in bright sunshine, for then the deadly reefs were visible as patches of yellow-brown against the clear green of the water. "In gloomy weather," Yonge wrote, "navigation was very difficult, owing to the dull color of the sea, while with the sun's rays low on the water and shining directly in the eyes of the masthead look-out, progress was impossible. Thus it happened that we could neither pass out through reefs in the early morning nor return through them in the late afternoon. If only the Barrier had been on the west instead of the east coast of Australia, how very much easier it would have been for us!"

To reach the extreme outer edge of the reef, the scientists boarded the *Daintree*, a motor launch piloted by an experienced skipper who had learned his way around the Barrier while collecting sea cucumbers for Chinese kitchens. As they neared the outer side, no reefs were visible except at low tide. The wind, blowing steadily from the east, made the launch's progress slow and painful, and sent cascades of water over its passengers.

Finally they came to the end of the reef. Here it grew close to the surface of the water. On the inner side of the Barrier, islands existed in many places where the coral had reached the surface,

but not here, for the surging waves of the deep ocean scoured
endlessly over the top of the reef. Yonge walked to the seaward
side of the reef and stared out at the endless ocean.

Here, all the fury of the Pacific waves spent itself against
this outlying ridge of coral. "Few memories will remain longer
in my mind," Yonge wrote, "than the sight and sound of these
Pacific breakers driven with the steady force of the south-east
Trade Wind, and breaking in a great line of foam upon the
cement rampart of the Outer Barrier. Towering far above, fifteen
or twenty feet high, they came curling over and hung poised
for a moment of time, gray-green and lowering under a dull,
storm-racked sky, to fall with the noise of thunder and in a
cascade of foam that came rushing in a swirling flood to the
summit of the reef."

There can be few places on earth more awe-inspiring than
this, where the world's greatest ocean collides with the world's
greatest coral reef. On the seaward side, the reef slopes downward for thousands of feet. Only the topmost two hundred feet
contain living coral; the rest is the tremendous platform of stone
that the polyps have built over the centuries as the floor beneath
them slowly subsided. Again and again, the waves slam against
the reef wall and draw back with a strange sucking noise, laying
bare the ragged outer edge of the reef platform for a moment
until the next wave.

"One was in the presence of forces far beyond the control,
and almost beyond the conception, of man," Yonge declared.
"Land was far out of sight, the horizon was bounded everywhere
by the gray, white-flecked, angry sea." The solid reef seemed a
miracle to him, as he thought in wonder of the lowly creatures
that had built it, "uniting, spreading, consolidating, resisting
the fury of the sea and the attacks of enemies, never resting nor
yielding, but converting the very substance of the sea itself into

a submarine mountain chain of limestone, against which even
the tempest-driven Pacific is utterly unavailing."

For C. M. Yonge, the Great Barrier Reef represented a wonderful scientific challenge. The findings of his expedition, published in six large volumes, added greatly to man's knowledge
of the world of coral. To most Australians, the Barrier is a major
tourist attraction. Boatloads of sightseers visit the inner reefs,
hunting for handsome shells, marveling at the profuse coral
growth, and keeping wary eyes out for such perils as stonefish
and cone shells. But to the first white man to see the Great
Barrier Reef, it was something out of a sea-captain's nightmare.

The discoverer of the Great Barrier Reef was Captain James
Cook, the greatest navigator of the eighteenth century. The
Yorkshire-born captain was forty years old when he set sail
from the harbor of Plymouth in 1768 on an ambitious expedition. Cook's assignment was to enter the South Pacific and carry
out certain astronomical observations of the planet Venus. He
was also instructed to search for an unknown southern continent
that many believed to exist somewhere in the Pacific.

Men had been looking for that *Terra Australis,* or Southern
Land, for more than two hundred years. In 1605, a Spanish
seaman named Torres discovered the big island now called
New Guinea, and sailed completely around it. Passing through
what now is named Torres Strait, which separates New Guinea
from Australia, Torres thought he saw land to the south, but
did not investigate. He may perhaps have brushed through
the northern fringes of the Great Barrier Reef, though he left no
record of it if he did.

Dutch explorers, a generation later, sailed past the southern
shores of Australia and patriotically gave it the name of New
Holland. But they did not follow up their explorations with a
trip along the eastern side of the continent. The Great Barrier

Reef remained undiscovered for more than a century. Of course, the natives of Australia had "discovered" the Barrier long ago. But they were savages who kept no histories, and in our vain way we have always considered a place unknown until a man of European origins has come upon it.

Cook's ship, the *Endeavour*, carried a small scientific staff. After sailing round Cape Horn into the Pacific, Cook headed for the lovely island of Tahiti, where the astronomical observations were performed in 1769. Then, looking for the mysterious Terra Australis, the expedition sailed southwest to New Zealand, which Cook explored for six months. Next Cook proceeded to Australia. On April 19, 1770, Europeans set eyes on Australia's east coast for the first time. They landed soon afterward at Botany Bay, a little south of the present city of Sydney.

The *Endeavour* moved northward up the coast. On June 10, Cook noted in his journal the presence of a "Small Low Island which lay about 2 Leagues from the Main; it being about high Water, about the time we passed it, great part of it lay under water." It was a coral island, the first Cook had sighted. All unsuspecting, he had been sailing within the Great Barrier Reef for the past 600 miles. Journeying up that broad channel, he had no inkling that he was steering his way over hidden shoals of coral, over a million sword-sharp reefs that, but for his good luck, could have ripped the bottom from his wooden ship.

When the truth came, it came violently. Sir Joseph Banks, a wealthy young man whose hobby was natural history, was aboard the *Endeavour* as part of the scientific staff. His diary entry for June 10 remarks, "While we were at supper [the ship] went over a bank of 7 or 8 fathom water which she came upon very suddenly; this we concluded to be the tail of the shoals we had seen at sunset and therefore went to bed in perfect security, but scarce were we warm in our beds when we were called up with the alarming news of the ship being fast ashore upon a rock."

Since they were far from the coast, they realized they must have grounded on a reef. Banks notes, "We were little less than certain that we were upon sunken coral rocks, the most dreadful of all others on account of their sharp points and grinding quality which cut through a ship's bottom almost immediately."

Cook remained calm. All hands were on deck, after that shuddering, terrifying shock of impact, and panic threatened until the captain's matter-of-fact attitude quieted things. He ordered the sails lowered and the boats hoisted into the water so the damage could be inspected. The situation was even worse than he might have feared. The ship had risen above a ledge of rock and was aground in a shallow basin of keen-edged coral.

Quickly Cook had the anchors broken out and fastened where the water was deepest, to starboard. The sailors turned the capstan, winding the anchor cables in the hope that the ship would be pulled toward the anchors and off the reef. The *Endeavour* did not budge. The sea surged against the hull, slamming it again and again into the coral, gouging chunks from the wood.

The next thing to do was to lighten the ship by jettisoning anything that could be spared. Cook's journal records, "We threw overboard our Guns, Iron, and Stone Ballast, Casks, Hoop Staves, Oil Jars, decayed Stores, etc." But the ship had run aground at high tide, and now the tide was ebbing, defeating the purpose of their work. As day broke, though they could see the land twenty-five miles away, it seemed as though they would perish on the reef.

A high wind had been blowing much of the night. Now it grew calm, easing the strain on the ship. At eleven in the morning, the tide began to rise, but the now much lighter ship, with fifty tons of equipment overboard, still did not lift. Water was entering through a ragged hole in the hull. The sailors hauled at the capstan, but the *Endeavour* would not move—and soon the tide was ebbing again.

Pumping desperately to keep ahead of the leak, Cook's men struggled to empty the water from the hold. At five in the evening, the tide rose once more, and four hours later the *Endeavour* was on even keel, though taking water as fast as or even faster than the pumps could get rid of it. It appeared certain that if they could get free of the reef at all, they would almost immediately sink, but Cook's cool and determined courage kept the crewmen at work. Another tide cycle came and went, and by twenty past ten, the water was again rising.

This had to be it. The ship could not stand much more of a battering against the reef. All hands were busy, either at the pumps or the capstans, and a fierce effort heaved the ship into deeper water. She floated! But water poured in through the gaping wound in the hull, and the sailors, exhausted by twenty-four hours of continuous effort, had to fight against fatigue as well as the sea. They pumped through the night, and in the morning, when a fair breeze from seaward arose, they raised sail and limped toward the distant shore.

One of the youngest officers now suggested a way of plugging the leak. He cut up a piece of sail and coated it with wool and other substances to make it waterproof. It was carried on lines under the ship, where suction drew it against the hole and plugged it for the time being. A few square feet of canvas kept the *Endeavour* afloat until it could find a safe harbor several days later.

Cook was startled by the appearance of the hole. "Scarce a splinter was to be seen," he wrote, "but the whole was cut away as if it had been done by the Hands of Man with a blunt-edge Tool." He understood, now, why the *Endeavour* had been spared from sinking. A jagged piece of coral had broken off after penetrating the hull, and had remained sticking in the gash it had made, blocking much of the inward flow of water.

Six weeks passed while the vessel was being repaired. During this time, the Englishmen had their first encounters with the Australian natives, both of the human kind and otherwise. One creature that perplexed them reminded Cook of some sort of wild dog, "but for its walking or running in which it jumped like a hare or a deer." Examining a dead specimen, he declared, "It bears no sort of resemblance to any European animal I ever saw." Captain Cook had discovered the kangaroo.

He was not finished with the Great Barrier Reef. When the *Endeavour* was ready, Cook gave orders to continue northward through the same coral-studded seas that had nearly taken their lives. Cautiously this time, the great navigator maneuvered through the risky waters. He was well aware of the nature of the enemy, now. Reefs lay all about, north and south, east and west. Making his way through the narrow channels, hemmed in by the mainland to his left and the terrible Barrier to his right, Cook hunted for some passage that would take him into the open sea once more.

"A Reef such a one as I now speak of," writes Sir Joseph Banks in his diary in August, 1770, "is a thing scarcely known in Europe or indeed anywhere but in these seas: it is a wall of Coral rock rising almost perpendicularly out of the unfathomable ocean, always overflown at high water commonly 7 or 8 feet, and generally bare at low water; the large waves of the vast ocean meeting with so sudden a resistance make here a most terrible surf, Breaking mountains high. . . ."

That white line of heaving surf stood before Cook as a goal, for he knew it marked the outermost shoals of the Barrier. On August 14, he found an opening in the reef and at last succeeded in reaching the deep sea. The route has been known as Cook's Passage ever since.

Escaping from the reef did not give Cook the safety he expected to find. The wind dropped, and the *Endeavour* was becalmed. A sailing vessel is helpless in quiet weather. As it sat motionless, fifteen or twenty miles out from the reef, the *Endeavour* suddenly was caught up in a reefward tide and was swept rapidly back toward the Barrier. Cook's journal entry catches the terror of that moment:

"About four o'clock in the morning we plainly heard the roaring of the surf and at break of day saw it foaming to a vast height, at not more than a mile's distance. Our distress now returned upon us with double force; the waves which rolled in upon the reef, carried us towards it very fast; we could reach no ground with an anchor and had not a breath of wind for the sails."

Boats were lowered into the water, and cables strung from them to the *Endeavour*. Men rowed frantically, trying to pull the ship back from destruction by sheer muscle-power alone. It was hopeless. By six in the morning, the vessel was only a few hundred yards from the outer edge of the reef, and, Sir Joseph Banks tells us, "driving on as fast as ever."

It was, he says, "a terrible moment." But then "a small air of wind sprang up, so small that at any other time in a calm we should not have observed it." The *Endeavour's* headlong rush toward the reef was halted; the men in the boats pulled harder, the sails filled with air, and the ship moved away from the reef.

The breeze came and went. Cook could not get his vessel safely clear of the reef. One solution presented itself: to get back inside the Barrier somehow, and anchor there until the weather improved.

A quarter of a mile ahead, the captain saw an opening in the reef, and sent one of the mates to examine it. He reported that it was not much wider than the *Endeavour* herself, but that there was smooth water within. Cook got the ship opposite the opening, but, as his journal entry reports, the tide was "gushing out like a Mill Stream, so it was impossible to get in." They were swept two miles out to sea on this current; then the tide turned and the

ship was carried like a bobbing cork back toward the deadly
Barrier.

Another opening in the reef appeared, narrow and dangerous.
In what must have been a miracle of seamanship, Cook rode the
tide inward, passing safely between the coral jaws of the opening,
and entered a calm, shallow inlet. "It is but a few days ago,"
Cook wrote, "that I rejoiced at having got without the Reef; but
that joy was nothing compared to what I now felt at being
safe at an Anchor within it."

Unwilling to risk another bout with that frightening outer
wall, Cook remained within the Barrier, sailing northward along
the coast. Sir Joseph Banks found an opportunity to study
"many curious fish and mollusca besides Corals of many species." With food supplies running low, the crewmen foraged
on the reef and brought in hundreds of pounds of giant *Tridacna*
clams. The *Endeavour*, battered and leaking, somehow held
together as Cook threaded a route along the inner edge of the
reef for the next three weeks. Then the coastline to their left began
to trend to the west, and the water deepened. Cook realized he
was entering Torres Strait, between Australia and New Guinea.
He went ashore and claimed the eastern coast of Australia in the
name of King George III, naming his place of landfall Possession
Island. And then, sailing westward into a clear channel, he bade
farewell to the Great Barrier Reef and headed for the Indian
Ocean.

Cook returned to the Pacific on his second voyage round the
world, between 1772 and 1775. He visited Australia again, but
only the southeast shore, and he did not venture a second journey
through the Great Barrier Reef. He saw a good deal of coral
elsewhere in the Pacific, though, and the naturalists of the expedition gathered enough information to demolish much of the
scientific confusion about coral that existed at that time. On that

same voyage, Cook sailed southward almost to the bottom of the world, proving that a land of perpetual ice covered the region about the South Pole. He did not reach the continent of Antarctica itself, but he was the first man to come so close to it. On a third voyage, in 1779, Captain Cook was killed by the natives of Hawaii while exploring the northern Pacific.

As the eighteenth century drew to its close, the British began to colonize Australia—sending unwanted convicts there at first, and later a more respectable breed of colonist. Settlements grew rapidly on the continent's coasts. It was still a rugged land of pioneers when Charles Darwin arrived there in 1836. Despite his interest in coral reefs, the course of the *Beagle* did not take him near the Barrier.

The growth of the Australian colony led the British government to desire more information about the mighty reef. In 1842 it sent two ships, H.M.S. *Fly* and *Bramble,* to survey the Barrier's many reefs and to chart and mark the channels between them as routes for merchant vessels. Beete Jukes, a naturalist accompanying this expedition, made the first detailed scientific study of the Barrier.

After Darwin's book on coral reefs and John Murray's answering theory a generation later, the "coral reef problem" occupied the attention of many scientists. Since the best-developed coral reef in the world was the Barrier, a number of important scholars made the long, hazardous voyage to Australia to study it. Most of them, viewing the rocky islands in the channel, came away convinced that Darwin had been right about the sinking of the land. Some, like the American naturalist Alexander Agassiz, who visited the Barrier in 1896, still insisted there had been no subsiding of the land. The cutting of the shoreline, he said, was purely the work of the sea, which had eroded the coast. He did not explain, though, how the sea erosion could have left so many islands and still have eaten so far into the land behind it. By 1928, when C. M. Yonge's Great Barrier Reef Expedition began its work, the Darwinian idea was generally accepted, at least as it applied to the Australian reefs.

The Great Barrier Reef dazes the mind and numbs the imagination. More than 1,200 miles of coral, a stony garden in the sea, glowing with all the colors of the rainbow, inhabited by a wonderland of strange and beautiful creatures—it seems fantastic, and is fantastic. But the most incredible part of all is the fact that the entire magnificent sprawling wall of coral is the work of soft, simple animals no bigger than ants.

8.

Islands of Coral

Captain James Cook belongs with Magellan and Columbus in the highest rank of the great explorers. What made Cook great was not merely his skill as a navigator, nor his gifts as a leader of men, nor his bravery under danger: he could think, also. He had a keen and searching mind, and wherever he went he tried to discover reasons and causes. Though he was no scientist, he understood the ways and methods of science.

Cook was an asker of questions. His journals and notebooks are full of knotty problems. He could not supply the answers, but it is sometimes a mark of genius simply to be able to ask the right questions. Cook asked.

One of the questions he asked concerned the formation of coral islands. Cruising the Pacific, he observed many islands whose underlying rock was clearly of a coral origin. In the journal he kept on his second great voyage, he made this entry in June 1774, while visiting an island that "consisted wholly of Coral rocks all overrun with shrubs, etc." He asked:

"If these Coral rocks were first formed in the Sea by animals, how came they thrown up, to such a height? Has this Island

been raised by an Earthquake or has the Sea receded from it?"
This was not a low atoll a few feet above the sea; it was a high,
rocky island whose cliffs were of coral stone.

The problem puzzled Cook and many men after him. Since
coral polyps die when exposed to air for any length of time, how
could the coral islands have been formed? How could the reef
creatures possibly have extended their kingdom into the open
air?

Darwin, with his theories of reef formation, did not offer any
answers to the problem of coral islands. He was concerned with
living reefs, below the surface of the water. If he had suggested
that the bottom of the sea is steadily *rising*, it would have explained the presence of coral islands. But Darwin said the floor
was sinking constantly. That would carry the reefs downward, or
at best keep them where they were, just below the surface. It certainly would not push them out of the water.

For the past hundred years, scientists have devoted careful
study to the coral islands. They have offered three explanations
for island formation:

1. Accumulation of dead coral on top of a reef through wind
and wave action.
2. Drops in the level of the sea around a reef.
3. Upraising of the ocean floor beneath a reef.

Two or even three of these processes may have taken place on
the same reef, of course. The result is the gradual creation of an
island. Millions of people now live on islands built entirely of
coral. Bermuda, the Florida Keys, some of the West Indian
islands, and hundreds of the isles of the Pacific were all brought
into being by the toiling polyps.

The process starts with a living coral reef—a fringing reef,
or a reef that has been turned into a barrier reef by the sinking

of the land along whose shores it first developed. The reef may be of any size, perhaps just a patch of coral a few hundred yards across, or possibly of great extent. One large reef that will someday be a coral island in the West Indies is the Saba Bank, southwest of the island of Saba, Netherlands Antilles. This six-hundred-square-mile reef has already begun to reach toward the surface.

Since the corals themselves can never grow beyond the tide limit to form dry land, a submerged reef would stay submerged forever if its rising depended only on coral growth. Other factors must come into play to build an island from a reef.

As the reef grows, it normally takes on a cup-shaped appearance under water. The corals on the outside, exposed to the deep, oxygen-rich water of the open sea, grow faster than the ones in the center of the reef, where the water is quiet. In time the outer rim of the reef is only a few feet below the surface, and may stand above the water an hour or two a day at low tide.

Now the coral-killing forces go to work. The rough sea pounds at the outer coral rim, breaking off pieces weighing many tons and hurling them on top of the living corals deeper within. Some of these coral boulders stick up above the waves even at high tide to form the beginning of a rampart. The hurricanes that rip through the tropics every year do their bit in adding to this line of upthrust boulders. Smaller fragments collect between the bigger ones, and the waves wedge them tightly into place. Coral grinds against coral to form sand; fish chewing at the rocks produce more sand; the coral-drilling worms and mollusks contribute more. The sand forms a kind of cement, holding everything together. A wall of rock exists now, though it may be only a few yards long.

As the process continues, the exposed rampart tends to take on a horseshoe shape, following the outer rim of the reef on which it rests. The waves break against it and their strength is directed away at each side. The wall grows longer, shaped by the waves that beat against it.

Behind the wall, where the waves can no longer reach, the water is now strangely calm over the reef. The living coral continues to grow, but it is meeting difficulties. Sand and bits of coral are showering down on it from the outer rampart, and, now that the water no longer is in swift motion, these fine particles collect, smothering the polyps. Heavy tropical rainfalls, pelting the reef with fresh water, can also kill the coral now that there is little sea action. C. M. Yonge tells of a fifteen-inch rainfall at low tide on the Great Barrier Reef: "The reefs must have been literally drowned in fresh water. Not only was every animal and plant on the surface of the reef killed, but destruction continued as deep as ten feet below mean sea level."

A coral graveyard appears in the middle of the reef. Jacques-Yves Cousteau writes of swimming through "a recent coral tragedy" in the Red Sea: "We swam through hundreds of yards of lacy gray stones falling in ruin with branches of broken dead corals strewn about."

The result is a lagoon, surrounded by a crescent-shaped platform of rock above the water. If the reef had an atoll shape to begin with, then the lagoon will have already existed, in the place where the inner island once was before sinking. If the reef had been a solid flat, the action of sand and stagnation will create a lagoon in the center, producing an atoll-like effect. Either way, the island-forming process goes on and on, as more and more boulders are heaped up on top of the reef, with sandy flats forming on the protected side of the rampart.

The horseshoe still remains open at one end. The opening may be dozens of miles across, at first. As it closes, another force operates to maintain the opening. The tides are rushing in and out of the lagoon on its open side, scouring away the sediments. The narrower the opening, the faster the tides will move, and the more intense is the scouring action. The ring may never quite close, since it becomes harder and harder to build up a bank of debris as the opening narrows. And because this opening is always on the leeward side, the one away from the wind, few coral boulders are heaped up there by storms.

The debris of coral that builds the wall of the new island may be piled ten or fifteen feet high. High seas can toss coral boulders as far as three to five hundred feet inward on this rampart. So eventually a narrow but ever-growing strip of rocky land appears, with the horns of the crescent pointing away from the wind.

And now, sand begins to accumulate on top of the cemented-together boulders. The grinding of the coral and the action of fish keep plenty of sand appearing, and the sea deposits this on the new wall. The wind scatters it about, and may pile up dunes twenty or thirty feet high. The sand cloaks the underlying coral boulders, hiding them almost completely on the windward side of the island.

Without vegetation, this sandy cover might blow away in the first really severe tropical storm to strike. But the next stage in the island's development is the arrival of seeds cast up by the sea. In the Pacific, the coconut palms are usually the first to appear. Coconuts from trees growing on other islands fall into the sea and drift until they are thrown up on land again. The nuts take root almost anywhere, even on a patch of barren sand. The palms, as they sprout, hold the sand together with their spreading roots.

Other seeds arrive on the wind, and take root also. Coconut leaves and husks, and the stems and trunks of dead plants, fall to the sandy floor and begin to decay. As they rot, they form a fertile soil, overlying the sand. Now other plants that will not grow in sand can get a foothold on the island. Insects mysteriously appear, some of them clinging to driftwood washed up by

A mangrove swamp in the West Indies

the sea, some of them flying immense distances to settle on the new island. They burrow in the decaying vegetable matter, aiding the formation of soil.

What exists now is a horseshoe-shaped island, with a cover of vegetation—ready for man to arrive, bringing with him his dogs and pigs and barnyard fowl.

The island still encloses a shallow lagoon that is ever more sandy and stagnant. The seaward edge of the island is the highest, and it slopes gently down to this enclosed body of water. Coral can no longer grow in the lagoon, for it is too silty; a few dwarfed and sickly coral heads may struggle on for a while in the deepest part of the lagoon, but eventually the piling up of sand kills them. The lagoon turns into a mud flat.

An unusual tree called the mangrove helps in the process of turning lagoons into land. Mangroves grow in swampy, muddy places, where the water is quiet. They send roots down through the salt water into the mud, forming complicated networks that block all entry. The red mangrove is the most common kind; it often reaches heights of fifty feet, rising on stiltlike roots that hold the trunk well out of the water. At low tide, the oozing mud of the swamp is exposed and the roots are in the open air; when the water returns, it swirls around the base of the tree, but the spreading tangle of roots keeps the mangrove from toppling.

A mangrove swamp is a dense, humid place, thick with flies and mosquitoes and slimy mud. In the Pacific islands, the swamps also harbor a type of crocodile adapted to life in salt water, but these dangerous creatures are unknown in the much smaller mangrove swamps of the West Indies.

It is not pleasant to travel through a mangrove swamp. Since the floor is of soft mud, passage on foot is practically impossible. Traveling by boat, at high tide, is scarcely less difficult, because the boat must be pushed and poled through the salty ooze. C. M. Yonge tells of a trip through a mangrove swamp on an island of the Great Barrier Reef. He describes it as:

> . . . a region of mud, of black and decaying stumps and dead trees that lay . . . like long-extinct reptiles wallowing in a steaming Jurassic swamp. Outside the southeasterly [wind] might be blowing its steady twenty-five miles to the hour, driving the surf with a continuous roar against the reef, but nothing of that penetrated the thick wall of the mangrove. Here was a deadly silence, broken strangely by the sound of our voices and the splash of our oars. . . . Impossible to believe that we were on a coral reef seven miles from land, separated by a bare hundred yards from a stiff breeze and a breaking sea, and not in the backwoods of the Amazon or Congo. . . .

The mangrove plays a key role in the creation of land in the lagoon. About the roots of the red mangrove and its smaller relative, the white mangrove, the mud gathers and settles. The roots hold it in place. The mud flats are thus able to grow higher, reaching upward around the mangrove roots until eventually the tree is surrounded by dry soil instead of the oozing mud that it prefers. This kills the mangrove; but now the way has been paved for an invasion of other plants better suited for life in such soil. The mangrove serves to transform salty marshes into useful land.

This strange tree, living as it does on stilts above salt water, has an equally strange way of reproducing. Most trees produce seeds that drop to the ground to sprout. Not the mangrove. Its seeds sprout while still attached to the parent tree. Mangrove seedlings cling to the older trees like green spikes. Sometimes they remain on the parent trees until they are three or four feet long, and the branch carrying them bends under their weight.

Usually, though, the mangrove seedlings drop off when they are about eight inches long. If the tide is out, they drop into the mud, and soon send out roots from the lower end and leaves from the upper. More often, they land in the water and are swept away, or are washed from the mud by the returning tide.

Now begins a strange odyssey. The little mangroves float out to sea by thousands, moving with the currents. Nothing can kill these sturdy seedlings. They are tossed high by tempest-driven waves, baked by the sun, drenched by the rain. On and on they drift, until some lucky tide casts them up on a muddy shore. As the seedling enters the shallows, it no longer floats horizontally. What will be its root end is pointing downward. A sharp point is at its tip, and the same tide that casts the seedling ashore drives it a few inches into the mud. Other mangroves may arrive on the same tide. As each one lands, it begins to grow, sending out roots that arch and spear into the mud to form a circle of supports. This web of roots grows, while the trunk of the mangrove shoots upward. Driftwood, rotting seaweed, fragments of coral, uprooted sponges, and other debris of the sea are swept by the water into the maze of roots. As this refuse gathers, land is being built. Whole islands can emerge where mangroves have settled on some shallow mud flat.

Mangrove seedlings travel astonishing distances during these tide-driven migrations. The same species of mangroves are found in the West Indies and on the Florida Keys as in the swampy jungles of West Africa. That means that the Equatorial Current must have carried young mangroves clear across the Atlantic— and probably some still make that journey. The mangroves of the Pacific islands, too, are closely related to those of the African and West Indian swamps. Perhaps they crossed from sea to sea in the days before Central America rose to block the passage, or maybe they were tough enough to survive the icy trip around the tip of Cape Horn. At any rate, it seems clear that mangrove seedlings can drift for thousands of miles before coming to rest.

A special community of life springs up in the dark, mysterious world of the mangrove swamp. The same tides that brought the mangroves to shore bring the young ones of many sea creatures, washed into the warm water of the mangrove lagoon. A certain type of oyster makes its home on the projecting roots of the mangroves, huddling together in clusters of fifteen or more on a single root. When the tide is out, these oysters are revealed—the only oysters in the world that grow on trees.

Like most oysters, the ones of the mangrove swamp are good to eat. That giant snail, the conch, wanders over the mud, using its powerful foot to pull the oyster shells apart in order to reach the tender creature within. On the Florida Keys, raccoons come out at night to dine on oysters, while in the Pacific islands other small animals prey on the mollusks. The shells of hundreds of generations of oysters drop into the mud, helping to bind it and strengthen it as the mangrove swamp slowly becomes dry land.

Fiddler crabs, with their one immense claw endlessly waving about, tunnel through the mud of the swamp. Their passageways bring oxygen into the mud, making it easier for the mangroves to breathe. Starfish crawl in the mud, seeking oysters. Odd burrowing shrimps and snails are also found in the mangrove community.

The process is slow but inevitable. The lagoon is filled. Now a complete island has risen where, unknown thousands of years before, the sea rolled over the living surface of a submerged coral reef.

It should be understood that the sinking of the ocean floor, as described in Darwin's theory, does not prevent formation of coral islands in this manner. So long as the coral reef grows as fast as or faster than the bottom is subsiding, the reef will remain close to the surface. And a reef near the surface can be transformed, as we have seen, into an island projecting above the water. True, the sinking of the land may still be going on—but at the rate of a fraction of an inch a century. The deposit of new soil on the island, created by the decay of vegetable matter, more than makes up for this sinking process and keeps the island above the waves.

There are other ways by which coral islands can come into being. They may be thrust up suddenly by the force of a volcanic eruption somewhere beneath the earth's crust. This has evidently happened to some of the Indian Ocean atolls, among others. The coral foundations of the islands are high above the water. No theory of gradual island formation could account for that. The earth's crust shifts constantly, though, as if a sleeping giant, stirring restlessly in the bowels of the planet, occasionally pokes a knee or an elbow against it. When that happens, an entire reef may be lifted clear of the water.

Or the sea level may drop—a different process, though the

effect is the same. Geologists have shown that the level of the sea off the Australian coast has dropped ten feet in the past 4,000 years. This has happened, apparently, in three stages—a drop of five feet, a second one of two feet, and a third of three feet. With each change in sea level, coral reefs were exposed, becoming dry platforms on which islands could form.

This is how the Florida Keys came into being. The western group of Keys, known as the Pine Islands, are made of limestone formed by ocean-bottom sediments that became solid without the help of coral polyps. But the eastern Keys are dead coral reefs. Both island groups were exposed when the level of the sea dropped. When the eastern Keys were living reefs, about 50,000 years ago, the sea stood 100 feet higher there than it does today. Much of southern Florida was under water. Then the world turned cold as one of the periodic ice ages began. Water was drawn from the sea by evaporation, and was dumped on the land of the north in the form of snow. Temperatures remained low, so the snow did not melt and run back to the sea. It stayed piled high on the frozen land—and the steady loss of water in the sea dropped the sea level around Florida by some thirty feet. That killed the topmost coral. The cold continued. There was another fairly abrupt drop in sea level, and another. The whole reef stood exposed.

The ice age ended, and the sea rose again. But it never quite got back to its old level. The islands of the eastern Keys are the parts of the reef that were high enough to remain above water after the melting of the glacial ice. In places, where erosion has cut into the rock, the structure of the ancient corals can clearly be seen.

In one way and another, then, coral islands rise from the sea. The unwearying polyps, building their wondrous gardens of stone, produce not only underwater fairylands teeming with life and stunning in beauty, but also solid land as dwelling places

A pelican taking off after landing in the sea,
St. John, Virgin Islands

for mankind. In the Pacific, on countless atoll islands, villagers
raise plantations of coconuts and breadfruit, yams and bananas,
in the soil that lies atop foundations of coral stone. In the
Bahamas and West Indies and on Bermuda, lavish hotels hug the
beaches, playgrounds for happy vacationers who may never
suspect how the islands were formed. Houses are built from
blocks cut out of the coral deposits. Roads are put down over
rough coral ridges. Coral is everywhere on these islands, with
their coral hills and coral pebbles and coral-born sandy beaches.
And in the sea the polyps continue to toil.

Let us go down to the beach once more, and stand on that white sandy curve. The water is like green glass before us. The white line of surf marks the reef in the distance, and an infinity of blue sea stretches toward the horizon.

A big brown bird wheels lazily in the sky, a pelican out for a meal. It circles over the water, sighting some tasty fish, and plummets like a stone, landing with a splash and coming up moments later with a full pouch. A faint breeze stirs the leaves of the shoreline trees. Sand crabs scramble sideways to safety as we walk to the edge of the sea.

Gentle wavelets lap the shore. Transparent water sluices up

A sea fan in the foreground, with elkhorn coral behind it and gorgonians in the background

over the coral rocks at the fringe of the beach. We see periwinkles and neritas clinging to the rocks, and the white, crater-
like shells of barnacles, and here and there the jointed plates of a
chiton. In the water, the dark shadows of the coral reef stand
out clearly against the white, sandy bottom. Their call is ir-
resistible.

We don masks and flippers and glide into the warm, crystal-
clear water. Outward we go, passing above clusters of sea urchins
who wave their black spines at us as we swim by. An elegant
angelfish crosses our path and continues unhurriedly on. Gleaming minnows wheel and dart, a thousand silvery needles moving
as if with one impulse, fleeing not us but the three somber-colored
squids who have descended on them. A mottled sand flounder
flaps across the sandy bottom.

Now the coral appears. Mustard-colored fortresses of fire coral
sprout from the rocks. The gray knobs of finger coral spread
over the bottom. Here a great green dome of brain coral sits,
bedecked with red and yellow tubeworm gills. There, delicate
staghorn coral grows, branching and branching again. The
narrow red tubes of sponges are below us, and the darker bulks
of the bigger kinds. Colorful fish by the hundreds flutter by, a
procession of ocean jewels. Gay anemones cluster against the
coral canyons. Gorgonians whip back and forth as the water
surges. Ahead of us, we see the massive, awesome outstretched
branches of the elkhorn corals.

We know that these solid stony structures are the work of
minute organisms of the animal world. We know that they draw
limestone from the sea, building ever more stately mansions for
themselves, creating the complex community of the coral reef.
We realize that these twisted, gnarled masses of coral are, perhaps, the seeds of the islands of tomorrow.

We drift onward, voyagers through space, floating magically
over a timeless, silent world. It is all quite wonderful, this

world of the coral reef, and it always will be, no matter how many times we visit it.

Its wonder will never fade, for us. But the coral world is no longer strange. As we make our way over its chasms and valleys, over its thronging multitudes of living things, past its bright colors and eerie shapes, we feel the joy of returning to a place we know well, and love dearly.

For Further Reading

The books in this group will provide more information about the sea and its creatures, and particularly the creatures of the coral reef. Books marked with asterisks have outstanding illustrations or are otherwise of special value to young readers.

BATES, MARSTON. *Where Winter Never Comes.* New York: Scribner's, 1952. A general survey of the tropics, covering many aspects of geography and natural history.

* BUTTERFIELD, ALFRED. *The Coral Reef.* New York: Odyssey Press, 1964. A pocket-sized handbook with fine color photographs by Jerry Greenberg and Ed Fisher.

* CARSON, RACHEL. *The Edge of the Sea.* Boston: Houghton Mifflin, 1955. Paperback edition, Mentor Books. A sensitive and well-informed survey of shoreline life from Maine to Florida, with a good chapter on the coral reefs of the Florida Keys.

* COUSTEAU, JACQUES-YVES. *The Living Sea.* New York: Harper & Row, 1963. Diving adventures in many parts of the world.

* ENGEL, LEONARD. *The Sea.* New York: Time Inc., 1961. A general survey, well illustrated.

* IDYLL, C. P. *Abyss.* New York: Thomas Y. Crowell, 1964. Mainly about deep-water life, but a good deal of information about other forms.

* JÄGERSTEN, GÖSTA. *Life in the Sea.* New York: Basic Books, 1964.

144

The text is skimpy but the close-up photographs by Lennart Nilsson are astonishing.

LANE, FRANK W. *Kingdom of the Octopus.* New York: Sheridan House, 1960. Paperback edition, Pyramid Books. All about the cephalopods.

ROUGHLEY, T. C. *Wonders of the Great Barrier Reef.* Sydney, Australia: Angus & Robertson, 1936. A naturalist's account.

RUSSELL, F. S., and C. M. YONGE. *The Seas.* London and New York: Frederick Warne & Co., 1963. New edition of an encyclopedic one-volume survey.

YONGE, C. M. *A Year on the Great Barrier Reef.* London and New York: Putnam, 1930. The popular report of the great 1928-29 scientific expedition to the Barrier.

TECHNICAL BOOKS AND OTHER SOURCES

BANKS, SIR JOSEPH. *The Endeavour Journal, 1768-71.* Edited by J. C. Beaglehole. Sydney, Australia: Angus & Robertson, 1962.

BASCOM, WILLARD. *A Hole in the Bottom of the Sea; the Story of the Mohole Project.* Garden City: Doubleday & Co., 1961.

BEEBE, WILLIAM. *The Arcturus Adventure.* New York and London: Putnam, 1926.

BUCHSBAUM, RALPH. *Animals Without Backbones.* University of Chicago Press, 1938.

COOK, JAMES. *The Journals of Captain James Cook on his Voyages of Discovery.* Edited by J. C. Beaglehole. London: Cambridge University Press, The Hakluyt Society, 1955, 1961.

DANA, JAMES L. *Corals and Coral Islands.* New York: Dodd, Mead, 1872.

DARWIN, CHARLES. *The Structure and Distribution of Coral Reefs.* First edition, 1842. Paperback edition, Berkeley: University of California Press, 1962.

DAVIS, WILLIAM MORRIS. *The Coral Reef Problem.* New York: American Geographical Society, 1928.

HICKSON, SYDNEY J. *Introduction to the Study of Recent Corals.* University of Manchester Press, 1924.

MOORE, RAYMOND CECIL. *Introduction to Historical Geology.* New York: McGraw-Hill, 1949.

WOOD-JONES, F. *Coral and Atolls.* London: Lovell Reeve & Co., 1910.

MAGAZINES AND SCIENTIFIC JOURNALS

BARRETT, CHARLES. "The Great Barrier Reef and Its Isles," *National Geographic*, September 1930.

BROOKFIELD, CHARLES M. "Key Largo Reef: America's First Undersea Park," *National Geographic*, January 1962. (See also "Florida's Coral City Beneath the Sea," by Jerry Greenberg, in the same issue.)

BURNETT, ALLISON L. "Enigma of an Echinoderm," *Natural History*, November 1961.

COUSTEAU, JACQUES-YVES. "Fish Men Explore a New World Undersea," *National Geographic*, October 1952.

DAWSON, E. YALE. "The Rim of the Reef," *Natural History*, June-July 1961.

JOURNAL OF GEOLOGY, July 1950. The entire issue is devoted to reefs.

LADD, H. S., and J. I. TRACEY, Jr. "The Problem of Coral Reefs," *Scientific Monthly*, November 1949.

LONGLEY, W. H. "Life on a Coral Reef," *National Geographic*, January 1927.

MINER, ROY WALDO. "Coral Castle Builders of Tropic Seas," *National Geographic*, June, 1934.

———— "On the Bottom of a South Sea Pearl Lagoon," *National Geographic*, September 1938.

NEWELL, NORMAN D. "Corals," *Natural History*, March and April 1959.

RASMONT, RAYMOND. "Sponges and Their World," *Natural History*, March 1962.

ROUGHLEY, T. C. "Where Nature Runs Riot," *Natural Geographic*, June 1940.

SCHROEDER, ROBERT E., and WALTER A. STARCK, II. "Diving at Night to a Coral Reef," *National Geographic*, January 1964.

ZAHL, PAUL A. "Creatures of Hawaii's Coral Reefs," *National Geographic*, October 1959.

———— "On Australia's Coral Ramparts," *National Geographic*, January 1957.

Index

147

NORTH
AMERICA

Bermuda

Fla.   Bahama Is.   *TROPIC OF CANCER*

Cuba

Pacific Ocean

Atlantic Ocean

EQUATOR

SOUTH
AMERICA

TROPIC OF CAPRICORN

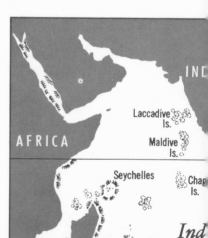

AFRICA

IND

Laccadive Is.

Maldive Is.

Seychelles   Chag Is.

Ind

MALAGASY REP.

Atolls

Barrier reefs

Fringing reefs

The World of Coral

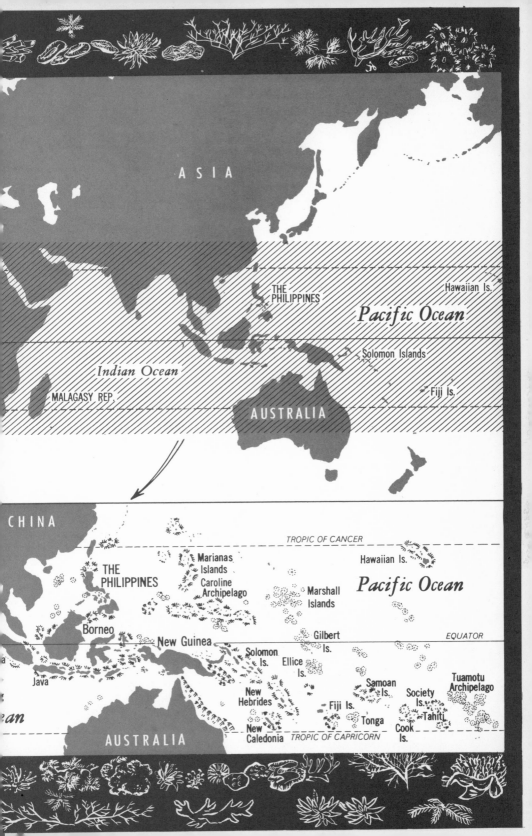

ASIA

THE
PHILIPPINES

Hawaiian Is.

Pacific Ocean

Solomon Islands

Indian Ocean

Fiji Is.

MALAGASY REP.

AUSTRALIA

CHINA

TROPIC OF CANCER

THE
PHILIPPINES

Marianas
Islands

Hawaiian Is.

Pacific Ocean

Caroline
Archipelago

Marshall
Islands

Borneo

Gilbert
Is.

EQUATOR

New Guinea

Solomon
Is.

Ellice
Is.

Tuamotu
Archipelago

Java

Samoan
Is.

Society
Is.

New
Hebrides

Fiji Is.

Tahiti

Tonga

Cook
Is.

AUSTRALIA

New
Caledonia

TROPIC OF CAPRICORN